The Psychology of Sleep

- Bolton Hall -

FOREWORD

This book is intended no less for those who do sleep well than for those who do not. It is just as important to be able to teach others to act well as to be able to do so ourselves. To teach we must analyze and comprehend our own action and its motives: for being able to do a thing well is far different from being able to teach it. In order to teach anything we must know how we do it and why others cannot do it. We never know anything thoroughly until we have tried to teach it to another.

Many persons sleep well only because they are still, like little children and animals, in the unreflective stage of life. That is the stage of the Natural Man, and it is good in itself; but later the mental life awakes, when consciousness of one's self begins, and examination of one's own desires develops. If not rightly understood or if not at least accepted, that development brings anxiety, unrest and disturbance of sleep, and breaks the harmony of the whole nature.

The highest stage of development is the spiritual, the all-conscious state which includes and harmonizes the other two. In that we do not lose the ready, overflowing enjoyment of our bodily exercises and functions; rather they are intensified; the physical and the mental are united in the complete life.

In order to attain this harmony we must examine the means that we and others use to gain rest and peace; some of these are instinctive and some prudential, and we must perceive why it is that these means work or fail to work in different cases. When, with all our getting, we have gotten this understanding, then, and not till then, all action becomes natural and joyful, for then we understand it all, and follow willingly the leading of the Spirit that is in Man.

> Care-charmer Sleep, son of the sable Night,
> Brother to Death, in silent darkness born.
> SAMUEL DANIEL.

CHAPTER I
SLEEP

Sancho Panza says: "Now, blessings light on him who first invented sleep! Sleep which covers a man all over, thoughts and all, like a cloak; and is meat for the hungry, drink for the thirsty, heat for the cold, and cold for the hot. Sleep is the current coin that purchases all the pleasures of the world cheap, and the balance that sets the king and shepherd, the fool and the wise man, even."—"Don Quixote."

S LEEPING is the one thing that everyone practices almost daily all his life, and that, nevertheless, hardly anyone does as well as when he began. We have improved in our walking, talking, eating, seeing, and in other acts of skill and habit; but, in spite of our experience, few of us have improved in sleeping: the best sleepers only "sleep like a child." It must be that we do not do it wisely, else we should by this time do it well.

Even the race of mankind as a whole does not seem to be able to use sleep, to summon it, or to control it any better than primitive man did. We talk much of the need of sleep, and sagely discuss its benefits, but we know neither how to use the faculty of sleep to the best advantage nor how to cultivate it.

Yet for ages men have studied the mystery of sleep. We have acquired many interesting facts concerning its variation, and have formulated a number of theories concerning its cause and advantages; nevertheless, science has given us little real knowledge of sleep, and less mastery over it.

Mankind has had idols ever since consciousness began. Advancing knowledge has changed the nature and number of the idols, but it has not destroyed them. The idol of the present age is "Science," and men worship it in the degree that it seems to fit their needs. They forget that Science is merely the knowledge of things and persons, arranged and classified, so as to make it available. In its nature it is fallible, for some new phase discovered to-day may show that yesterday's conclusion was formed from a theory which itself was based on a mistaken premise. Man has caught a glimpse of something that resembled truth, has stated it, reasoned about it, and finally either established its authority or disproved it utterly through the discovery of the real thing he was seeking. Either result was progress, because man grows, as Browning says, "through catching at mistake as midway help, till he reach fact indeed." So there is no need to be disturbed by the conflicting opinions of men of science touching the purpose or method of sleep. Even the rejected theories have added to the sum of our knowledge, and the field for investigation is still open to all who are faithful in noting and comparing the manifestations of Nature, which the scientists call phenomena.

Most of what we call science has to do with physical or material things. Consequently, we find scientists dealing mainly with what may be called tangible phenomena, those which may be measured or weighed or held in the hand or, at least, pinned down by pressure of thumb or finger.

Material Science's estimate of man is largely gauged by

> "Things done, that took the eye and had the price;
> > O'er which, from level stand,
> > The low world laid its hand,
> Found straightway to its mind, could value in a trice."

This is the almost inevitable result of looking upon life as purely material or physical. We must view life as physical, but not physical only; as mental, but not mental only; as spiritual, but not spiritual only.

In studying sleep and its attendant phenomena all these things must be taken into consideration. So slight a thing as fancy may profoundly influence our acts; fancies not attributable to any material source, so fleeting and evanescent that the clumsy net of language cannot hold them, may induce sleep or destroy sleep.

A review of the theories and conclusions of physicians, both scientific and unscientific, as well as of others who have found the study of sleep of absorbing importance, will find a place in our examination of this vital function of organisms.

CHAPTER II
HOW MUCH SLEEP

Six hours in sleep, in law's grave study six,
Four spend in prayer, the rest on Nature fix.
                  (Translation.) SIR EDWARD COKE.

M AN is the highest expression yet discovered of the "living organism," and sleep has always taken more of his time than any other function. Marie de Manacéïne of St. Petersburg, in her great book called "Sleep," says: "The weaker the consciousness is, the more easily it is fatigued and in need of sleep; an energetic consciousness, on the contrary, is contented with periods of sleep that are shorter, less deep, and less frequent." Although the consciousness of the race has developed and strengthened enormously, and is steadily strengthening itself, the old-fashioned idea that one-third of our time should be spent in sleep holds the average mind as strongly as ever. We insist upon it for the young, impress it upon everybody, and look distrustfully upon him who is so daring and unreasonable as to say that he requires less than eight hours of sleep. When an idea is intrenched in the mind it is next to impossible to drive it out by reason or even by repetition.

It is the popular belief that Alfred the Great—who is also Alfred the Wise and Alfred the Good (being dead so long)—divided time into three equal parts, and taught that one part should be given to sleep. If he had said this, it would not follow that it is the last and wisest word on the best way to divide our time, but he did not say it. What he said was that one-third of each day should be given to sleep, diet and exercise: that is, that a man should devote eight hours to sleeping, eating and whatever form of exercise or recreation he desired.

There is nothing to show that Alfred spent even six hours in sleep, although there is plenty of proof that he recognized the difference between rest and sleep, for he gave the second division of the day—eight hours—to study and to reflection, while the remaining eight hours were to be for business. In those days kings worked hard. Sir Henry Sumner Maine says that the list of places where King John held court shows that even he was as active as any commercial traveler nowadays. ("Early Law and Custom," p. 183.)

But the superstition that Alfred recommended eight hours for sleep will not down, and no amount of argument or proof will change the opinion of the average man on this point. "Our forefathers slept eight hours," they say; "so should we." We forget that probably the rushlight and the candle had much to do with the long hours of sleep in olden times. As artificial light has improved, sleeping-time has been shortened.

There is an old English quatrain which runs:

"Nature requires five,
   Custom gives seven,
Laziness takes nine
   And wickedness eleven."

But sleep is a natural need, and, like any other natural need, varies in degree in different persons. Dogs, cats and other animals generally sleep more than we do, and their young ones sleep still more. Generally speaking, the infant, whose mental powers have barely awakened, who is, so far as we can tell, merely a human animal, needs more sleep than it will ever need again in its existence. In this great need of sleep the human animal resembles other animals.

It frequently happens that, as a man waxes older, he requires less and less sleep than in his growing and most active years. But old people who have outlived their mental life come to a time when they sleep and perform merely the physical functions like the infant; so also with those whose energy so far exceeds their physical strength that the mere effort of living exhausts them. This condition may be in part due to overstrain of the powers of youth and middle age, but it also follows the fixed idea that years diminish strength and lessen energy. It is easy to fall into this notion, for it accords so well with the general idea that rest must come only after the period of activity, whether that period be a day or a lifetime.

All of us have had periods when we have needed fewer than our average hours of sleep. People who sleep out of doors or in thoroughly ventilated rooms, under warm but light clothing, find that they need less sleep than when they occupy poorly ventilated rooms and wrap themselves in heavy, unhygienic clothing. Fresh discoveries are being made almost daily by those who give intelligent consideration to these things.

Even babies differ in their need of sleep. I know one healthy, happy, beautiful baby who has never slept the average sixteen hours that babies are supposed to need. This child is now between three and four years of age, and has never gone to sleep before nine or half-past nine at night. Her parents had the common idea of long hours of sleep for infants, and the child had a hard struggle for a while to convince them that she had no such need: such struggles are often called "naughtiness." She was regularly put to bed at seven o'clock, and all the usual devices for enticing a baby to sleep were practiced. Sometimes she was left severely alone, sometimes she had gentle lullabies sung to her, but, whether alone or in company, this particular baby played and enjoyed herself until between nine and nine-thirty, when she quietly dropped to sleep. She awoke as early as the average baby wakes, happy and refreshed, and her parents finally learned that there is no sleeping rule that has no exceptions, whether applied to infants or adults.

Drowsiness is a sign that we ought to sleep, just as hunger is a sign that we ought to eat. Natural wakefulness means that we ought not to sleep. The child tries to obey the promptings of nature, but we think these promptings are wrong, if not wicked, and force him into all sorts of bad habits. Says Michelet, "No consecrated absurdity could have stood its ground if the man had not silenced the objections of the child." We are slowly learning that there is no need or function of the body or of the mind that is exactly the same in all individuals, or that is always the same even in the same individual.

But, in spite of this dawning knowledge, we still view with alarm any disregard of the rule, either in ourselves or another; so true it is, as Thomas Paine says, that "It is a faculty of the human mind to become what it contemplates." We have looked upon ourselves as having certain, unvarying, imperative needs until we have almost become subject to them.

CHAPTER III
THE TIME OF SLEEP

"Women, like children, require more sleep normally than men, but 'Macfarlane states that they can better bear the loss of sleep, and most physicians will agree with him.'"

H. CAMPBELL.

THE amount of sleep, like the amount of food, required by an individual varies greatly, depending largely upon the conditions at the time. Edison, for instance, can go days without sleep when engrossed in some invention, and he has been quoted as saying that people sleep too much, four hours daily being quite sufficient.

In answer to my inquiry, Mr. Edison's secretary wrote, "Mr. Edison directs me to write you that the statement is correct, that for thirty years he did not get four hours of sleep per day." Evidently, experience taught him that an average of four hours per day, if taken rightly and at the right time, is enough for him. He keeps a couch in his workroom so as to sleep when he is sleepy. He does not need a clock to tell him when to go to bed, any more than you need a thermometer to tell you when to pull up the blankets.

Edison is not alone in his views on sleep. He made extensive experiments with the two hundred workers in his own factory which convinced him and most of them that the majority slept much too long. The hands seem to have entered willingly into the trials: perhaps their personal regard for him influenced their conclusions. Napoleon Bonaparte and Frederick of Prussia were both satisfied with four hours of sleep,[1] while Bishop Taylor was of opinion that three hours was sufficient for any man's needs, and Richard Baxter, who wrote "The Saints' Rest," thought four hours the proper measure.

Paul Leicester Ford, who was never a strong person, once told me that he found four hours' sleep enough for all purposes. He did not wish to be understood as saying that four hours' rest was enough, but four hours' sleep. He was one of the few who understood the difference between sleep and rest. He frequently rested; his favorite practice being to lie back in a big armchair with a book, and forget the surrounding conditions. The book created a different set of sensations, which, combined with the pause in physical activity, brought a sense of rest to the frail body. He frequently got his four hours of sleep curled up in the big chair, and was then able to go on with the work which in a few short years made him famous. The wife of the late George T. Angell of Boston testifies that for years he seldom slept four hours a night, having found that, for him, more was unnecessary; but, of course, it does not follow that no more is necessary for anyone.

These are not unusual instances, but rather typical cases. History and biography are full of such; each of us can probably mention one or more persons among his own acquaintance who can do well with less than the usual eight hours of sleep, but we have looked upon them as exceptions and perhaps have prophesied that they will feel the evil results later, if not now. We usually select ourselves as the standard for all other persons, or perhaps it is more correct to say that we are prone to select one stage of our own development as a standard, and try to compel even our growing self to conform to that stage. When the crab outgrows his shell it sloughs off, and, so far as we know, he offers no objection, but takes the new shell, which answers his needs better. But we, who consider ourselves infinitely superior to the crab, try to compel ourselves to keep within the bounds of old thoughts, early habits, and outgrown customs after we no longer need them. When we are unfortunate enough to succeed, we rejoice at our cramped souls as the Chinese woman prides herself upon her crushed, cramped, misshapen foot.

The amount of sleep that suited you last year may not suit you to-day. You may really be getting better sleep and so needing less of it: or you may have to make up by quantity for a poorer quality. The test is that, if you are sleepy in waking hours, you need better sleep or more of it. If you are wakeful in sleeping hours, you need less sleep or else you are not getting the right kind. Good sleep is a habit, a natural habit as distinguished from an acquired habit, and when we learn to take it naturally, and in natural amount, we get a great deal more from it. It is fair to assume that purely natural habits, which continue from age to age through all stages of human progress, are essential to human welfare. Otherwise they would drop away from us as many useless physical parts have dropped. If you stop to think of this, you know that it is so; the man in the street and the girl at the ribbon counter do not know, so there is more excuse for them if they misunderstand. It may be that they usually sleep better than you do, and so do not need to know it.

CHAPTER IV
WHAT SLEEP MAY MEAN

O Sleep, we are beholden to thee, Sleep,
Thou bearest angels to us in the night,
Saints out of heaven with palms.

JEAN INGELOW.

WE know so little about sleep, positively, that anyone may assume one thing or another about it, so long as what he assumes accords with what we do know positively.

It has been surmised that, during sleep, the subconscious mind is busy with the day's impressions of the objective mind,[2] fitting and relating them to past experiences, the sum of which makes up the man himself. The subconscious mind is, in a sense, man's attitude to life. It receives suggestions more easily than the objective mind receives them, and has more effect upon man's understanding of life. If our last conscious thought is a loving thought toward all living things, we have aided the latent mind in its effort to get in tune with the infinite harmony of life. Alice Herring Christopher, the metaphysician, once told me that every night as she drops off to sleep she says to herself that she is going to have a lovely time, and as a consequence she does; and that, on waking, she tries to realize how delightful her sleep has been.

There is an old saying that, when a baby smiles in its sleep, it is because the angels are whispering to it, and, if we kept ourselves in communion with the substance of things, "angels" might bring us sweet messages, too. They surely will, if we drop to sleep as lovingly and peacefully as a little child.

Another friend of mine, who has the faculty of wearing herself out with the excitement of each day's experiences, is learning to offset this unnecessary drain upon her strength by suggesting to herself each night, "I shall wake rested and refreshed in the morning." By this means she is gaining in nervous poise, and averting the numerous "break-downs" from which she used to suffer. Having made this much progress,—which brings her "not far from the kingdom,"—it only remains for her to make the full claim for the fulfillment of the promise, "Ye shall find rest to your souls," to secure it.

For the most part, men still regard sleep as a symbol of death, that time when we shall know nothing of what goes on about us; when, according to general belief, we no longer grow or enjoy. We exclaim with Hesiod, "Sleep—the Brother of Death and the Son of Night!" But the new idea of sleep as a growing time is overcoming that old idea of sleep as death, and is beginning to rob even the great change itself of its terrors. We are beginning to see that sleep does not interfere with the activity of the mind, but simply gives it an opportunity to digest and absorb impressions. In the same way it may be that death does not interfere with the activity of the real man, but may afford him an opportunity to get the full meaning of the experiences he had while sojourning in the objective world.

As it is not conceivable that life began with our individual appearance in this world, so it is not likely that it will end when our individual consciousness ceases. The sum of what we have learned and of what we have done must go on, else all the learning and the doing would be for naught. So this thing which was "I"—and will continue to be the sum of that "I," no matter whether I am conscious of it or not—will use and absorb all that has been thought or done in the body, and accept or reject its results.

It will all count in that next experience, and help us to be, as Browning says:

> "Fearless and unperplexed
> When I wage battle next,
> What weapons to select, what armor to endue."

The sum of our experiences added to the sum of all that have gone before will help us to understand life better when and wherever we are again conscious of it, just as the experiences of each day help us to live the next day better. In the active, waking world the perceptive mind receives impressions which the reflective mind stores up and brings to bear upon our daily life and thought, thus developing greater consciousness in the individual; so the interruption of all physical activity may be necessary to the further development of the real and intangible man.

As one awakes each morning from a night's sleep a new man, physically and mentally, although not necessarily aware of any change, so may our awakening be from the last sleep that men call death. It may be that we shall arise to new experiences, or perhaps to further development in a world that we cannot touch with our hands. But in either case we may not doubt that the awakening will be good, for all life is good. For, after all, we should know none of the joys of living if we had not tried them. Life is consciousness, and hardly one of us would prefer never to have lived; to have had no share in that which has meant *man*; the growth and culmination of unnumbered centuries. Life is one, a whole, and the "slings and arrows" of daily worries and toil are only an unimportant part of it. And, if it is so good that we wish to stay here and hope to enjoy it, if we can see how it has steadily improved and beautified in the ages that have passed, we cannot fail to see that all it may yet become will also be good.

CHAPTER V
HOW TO GO TO SLEEP

Sleep sweetly, tender heart in peace!
TENNYSON.

MAN craves sleep. If we know of a friend who is suffering in body or mind we wish him sleep; mothers soothe their pain-racked or terrified children to sleep with every gentle art known to them; if, for any reason, man is out of harmony with his life as he sees it, he instinctively turns to "Nature's sweet restorer." It is a sovereign balm for many ills, yet we seldom recognize wherein its virtue lies. During his waking hours man is frequently at odds with his surroundings. He is out of tune with the real things of life and is apt to mistake the material side of his life for the whole of his being. But when sleeping he is less hampered with the impressions of the workaday world, less resistant, and, therefore, more harmonious. It is in this mental relaxation that the true benefit of sleep consists.

We have as yet no conception of the immense import of suggestion to ourselves or others as a cure for body or mind. Suggestions may often be made to a person sound asleep, but they are most effective just at the time when the reason and the will are losing control of the mind, although consciousness has not yet lost its grip.

Accordingly it helps our growth to relax the whole nature before going to sleep and to drop into the mind the thought of peace and harmony; the assurance that all is and must be well. To do this is to get the best sort of sleep, the sleep that binds us closer to our fellows and makes us feel the oneness of all life. This is the sleep from which we awake refreshed, ready to take up the day's duties cheerfully. It is an old country saying, when a person seems what is called "out of sorts" in the morning, that "he got out on the wrong side of the bed." But it is much more likely that he went to sleep in the wrong way: that is, in an unloving frame of mind.

"Let not the sun go down upon your wrath" has a wider significance than we usually realize. As a matter of mere physical well-being, if we have allowed the lack of knowledge or the selfishness of our brother to annoy or irritate us, it is well to wipe away all traces of that irritation before lying down to rest. It is well, when possible, to seek the "little one" we have offended, through our own ignorance or selfishness, and make our peace by confessing the fault; while, if we are still self-centered enough to feel that our brother has dealt harshly with us, we may remove all the sting by thinking lovingly of him. As the soft answer turneth away wrath, so the soft attitude turneth out wrath, both from ourselves and from him. Each day should complete itself. Sufficient unto the day is the good and the evil thereof, and to attempt to carry over the evil through resentment until another day is but to lay up trouble for ourselves.

For, after all, it is lack of knowledge or understanding that makes our brother unkind to us or us to him. Each is doing the best he can, being such a man as he is. Each of us has still some of that separateness which makes us regard our own interests as apart from other interests, or hostile to them. What our brother does, therefore, he does because it seems to him the best thing for himself. As soon as he sees that one cannot truly prosper at the expense of another, because we are all one, he will give up his stupid ways —as we shall give up our stupid ways when we see that same truth. Until then it is useless to be angry or upset, for that is only to show that we, too, are unable to see the oneness of all. As it is bad for our brother that he is so blind, it were more consistent that we should feel sorrow than anger at his self-injury.

Epictetus understood that, nineteen hundred years ago, and we have not become so stupid as to deny it; we only forget. He saw that there is only one kind of motive in all men—they are moved by what they think is right and best for themselves. Said he, "It is impossible to judge one thing best for me and to seek a different one, to judge one thing right and be inclined towards another." We all know this about ourselves, but we do not see it so plainly about others.

If we felt this about all men, we should not have "indignation with the multitude." For what are all their wrongdoings? Is it not that they are "mistaken about the things that are good and evil? Shall we then be indignant with them, or shall we only pity them?... Show them the error and we shall see how they will cease from it when they really see it. But, if they do not see the error, they have naught better than the deceptive appearance of the thing as it looks to them." For, argues Epictetus, "this man who errs and is deceived concerning things of the greatest moment is blinded, not in the vision that distinguished black and white, but in the judgment which distinguished Good and Evil.... If it is the greatest misfortune to be deprived of the greatest things, and the greatest thing in every man is a *Will* such as he ought to have, and if one be deprived of this, why are we still indignant with him?... We need not be moved contrary to Nature by the evil deeds of other men. Pity them rather, be not inclined to offense and hatred.... When someone may do us an injury or speak ill of us, remember that he does it or speaks it, believing that it is meet and best for him to do so. It is not possible, then, that he can do the thing that appears best to you, but the thing that appears best to him. Wherefore, if good appears evil to him, it is he that is injured, being deceived. For, if anyone takes a true consequence to be false, it is not the consequence that is injured, but he is injured who is deceived. Setting out, then, with these opinions, you will bear a gentle mind toward any man who may injure you. For, say on each occasion, 'so it appeared to him.'" Forgive: and if you must blame somebody, blame yourself—you can forgive yourself so easily.

So we shall find sleep more restful if we leave behind us all the shortcomings of ourselves and of our fellows, and approach that season of seeming forgetfulness with love towards all. Calm as an infant's sleep will be the slumber of the all-loving man, and for him the new day will dawn with increased brightness; his strength shall be renewed, and his joy be more abundant.

If we always lie down to sleep with this attitude, regarding the darkness not merely as the time when the physical man should rest, but also as a growing time for the spiritual man, it will not be long before we adjust our daily life to more harmonious relations with the universe. The more lovingly we live, the sweeter and sounder will be our slumber, for so it is that "He giveth his beloved sleep."

CHAPTER VI
SLEEP IS NATURAL

Sleep is the joy of life.
Wu Ting Fang.

MAN has not gone so far beyond the animal stage of development as to have cast aside all the weights that hinder him in his further progress. He has considered three substantial meals daily necessary to his health, and if, for any reason, his system refused to take that quantity of food, he has worried himself almost into a fever over it. Or, he has consulted a physician who has usually given him a tonic; a tonic is something to stimulate the jaded appetite, or compel the surfeited stomach to do more work than it should.

Recent research has shown that this overworking of the digestive organs is a fruitful source of physical disease, that it dulls the mind and chills the spirit. Our loving Mother Nature punishes each excess, because pain quickest draws our attention to our wrongdoing. The flesh strives with us as well as the Spirit, for we reap in our own bodies the fruit of our ways; still man looks everywhere but within for advice and counsel. His feelings may warn him that he is pursuing the wrong course, but, until some authority has assured him that he is doing wrong, he rarely pays heed to his inner warnings.

Gluttony is one of the evils which Nature tries to save man from. The stomach rebels when it is made to dispose of too much material, and calls in the rest of the body to assist in making a protest. The head aches, the heart works uneasily, the liver and bowels become inactive, the limbs grow heavy, and the whole abused man is ill at ease. A bad breath is worse than an evil spirit, and a bad digestion is a surer sign of ill-doing than a bad conscience. Nature has done her best to show the foolishness of overeating; it is not her fault if man persists in this course in spite of her warnings, but she takes care that he pays the price of his wrongdoing, sometimes in sleeplessness, often in even more serious ways.

Overeating has been the fashion for centuries. We have thought that, the more we eat, the stronger we should become, and mankind has followed that fashion despite the ills that it has caused, forgetting that it is what we digest, not what we eat, that nourishes. The effects of overeating are both direct and indirect. The direct effects are those that dog the heels of the offense. These effects, when acute, have even caused death in a few hours or days, as with King John and his "dish of lamprey eels," but some of the indirect effects are more direful. Much of the use of alcoholic liquors is due to overeating. When we have eaten too much, and the digestive organs are so overloaded that they cannot work, we take alcohol in some form to stimulate them to greater action. As we continue the wrong practice, it requires more and more liquor to stimulate us, usually ending in stupor, a parody of sleep. In a short time that which we used to cure or offset one evil has created a habit, in itself a greater evil.

It took us a long time to see the connection between illness, drunkenness, and overeating. We now know that drink becomes a habit and after that a disease. If we look at mankind in the mass, drunkenness appears plainly as the result of two general causes, overstimulation of the indulgent classes, and the malnutrition that craves stimulants in the masses of the underfed.

Like every other faculty, consciousness becomes dulled through lack of exercise. It follows that oversleeping inclines to dullness and stupidity. Further, the body will readily accommodate itself to the physiological conditions that prevail during sleep, to a changed blood circulation, and breathing. The oversleeping may come to resemble the hibernation of some animals. For those inclined to drowsiness or to unnaturally long sleep, real interests in life are helpful, also amusements, pleasant society in the evenings, and even tea and coffee or other mild stimulants are useful.

Meanwhile, some people, at least, think they suffer from insomnia, who in fact suffer from going to bed too soon or lying abed too late—in the struggle to sleep more than they need.

CHAPTER VII
THE DUPLEX MIND

Millions of spiritual creatures walk the earth
Unseen, both when we wake and when we sleep.
MILTON.

W E must not forget that it is easy to miss the good results of any natural function, and, through misuse, get only poor results. As in the matter of eating, we should get only good from satisfying our hunger, but the acquired habit of eating more than we need or can digest does incalculable harm. In the same way we may misuse sleep, and so lose its best benefits.

"Sleep that knits up the raveled sleave of care," may be made, as Shakespeare says, a repairing time as well as a resting time, for as Iamblichus, the Neo-Platonic philosopher saw, "The night-time of the body is the daytime of the soul." With some insight into the best uses of this natural habit, Iamblichus further said that, during sleep, "the nobler part of the soul is united by abstraction to higher natures and becomes a participant in the wisdom and foreknowledge of the gods." Dr. Thomas J. Hudson's claim made a very popular appeal, that there is a subjective mind made up of our inner knowledge, our own intuitions and mental processes. He alleged it to be a part of our being that is able, in some instances—as in the case of "lightning calculators," of mind-readers and of some clairvoyants— to perceive the relations of things without reasoning them out, and to perceive the fixed laws of Nature without the aid of the senses.[3] He concluded that this mind or this faculty of mind is an inheritance from experiences and conclusions of the race in its upward growth.

Swedenborg also, who was at least a noted scientist, divided the mind into the Interior, corresponding to the subjective mind, and the Exterior or reasoning memory.[4]

The objective mind, as it may be called, is what we all know as mind or intellect, that part which deals with external objects, getting its impressions and reaching its conclusions from observation. It is differently affected in different individuals by such purely physical things as sight and hearing. For a proof of this, ask any two persons who have seen and heard and been affected by something you have seen and felt, to describe its effect upon them, and the mental picture they have of it. Not only will they not agree in detail with each other, but you will find that neither has seen it in the same way that you have.

Modern science cannot accept the statement that foreign, mysterious agencies control the mind during sleep; but may not some such experience as that which Iamblichus describes, come to us in sleep by the spirit working, not from without, but from within us? Our spiritual nature is freed at night from the incessant calls that beset us during the day. In the calm that comes over it in the night-time the doors of the storehouses of memory may stand wide open before it, and it may lead perhaps a broader, fuller life.

Professor William James has shown that in our waking hours, each of us is not so much a single self as a cluster of separate selves—a business self, social self, the material self, and so on—all making up the man as his casual acquaintances know him. Professor James found that in every individual there is rivalry and sometimes discord among these partial selves. Now may it not be that in the silence, these warring factions lose their identity in a state of broader conscious life, and merge themselves into a harmoniously acting "Spiritual Me"?

From the standpoint of this spiritual self, then, the waking state shows only the objective aspects of the mind. It is that understanding which shows us all men working, whether willingly or unwillingly, for the common good, and each receiving what he needs or has power to use. It is a recognition that all men are comprehended in the Spirit's plan, that nothing can be for the common harm; that even mistakes work out for good, and that life gives to each the experience from which he will get most development and the power which he can best use and relate to his whole life. From the spiritual standpoint the subjective mind is the indwelling life of the soul; and its growth a matter of gradual self-attainment. At its highest stage it is the realization of that which we have in common with everyone— that understanding and that consciousness of the law of harmony which makes us love all mankind, and live in communion with the love that is the substance of all things. The separate self does not appear at all on the horizon of such thought and purpose.

We have all had a consciousness of this love at some time in our lives, no matter how the cares of the world may have choked it out. It was this consciousness that made a little boy say, in a burst of happiness, "I love everything, and everything loves me." When we "become like a little child" in this sense, we, too, recognize the love that binds all life in one.

When we can harmonize these two—the subconscious, that knows no separate self, with the objective, that can see all men as one because it sees all men as working for the same end—we shall have rest and harmony instead of worry, the insanity of the spiritual mind.

The objective mind which is active during waking hours, apparently rests during sleep; the subconscious mind is ever busy. Like the heart or the digestive organs, the subconscious mind carries on its work during that break in our usual consciousness which we call sleep. How this is done we do not know, any more than we know how the physical organs carry on their work while we are wrapped in slumber and unconscious of all about us. There are very few, though, who have not had some proof of the activity of the latent mind during sleep. That somehow this under-mind does work in an "uncanny" way—that is to say, in an unknown way—is shown by the fact that most persons can wake up at any hour that they fix in their minds without being called and without the abominable alarm clock.

It is a common enough thing to hear people say, "I do not know how I knew that; I never remember hearing it; it just came to me." Or, "I tried and tried to think of that yesterday, and could not, but, when I woke this morning, it was the first thing that came to my mind." Such incidents show that some process of which we are not objectively conscious is going on all the time; that no mental experience is destroyed or wholly dissipated. The common wish is "to sleep over" any perplexing matter. After a good sleep our ideas are often better arranged than when we fell asleep.

I have a friend who drops all her problems into her subconscious thought, refuses to be "exercised in her mind" about them, and leaves them for the latent mind to answer. So long as she views them from the objective, conscious point of view only, she finds herself worrying and losing sleep. The sleep-won mind, the "all-knowing Self," as it were, is not touched by worry, perhaps because, in communion with the substance of all experience, it perceives that there are few "problems" in life, when she does not persist in regarding as a "problem" each separate experience.

We must learn to connect each experience with what we know of our life up to that point and with what we think it is meant to be. This effort will often show us, or itself prove to be, the key to the "problem." But it is only the scientific expert, one who has a perfect conception of the workings of all the parts of the frame, who can take one bone and reconstruct from it the entire structure of the extinct animal. That would be impossible for the tyro, and most of us are tyros in the science of living.

CHAPTER VIII
WAKEFULNESS

And Sleep will not lie down but walks
Wild-eyed and cries to time.
"Ballad of Reading Gaol."

OSCAR WILDE.

THE fact that we confound rest and sleep makes us regard wakefulness as an evil. We go to bed to sleep, and, if sleep does not come at once, we begin to fret and to toss and we try by every means that we know to force ourselves to sleep. We never accomplish anything that way, because it is essentially opposed to the nature of sleep. Sleep, to be refreshing, must be complete relaxation of mind and body, and that is not gained by striving. Natural sleep is merely "letting go," which is just what so many find hard to do. The course is so simple and plain that "the wayfaring man, though a fool, *need* not err therein," but he often does err in spite of its simplicity; and sometimes, perhaps, even because of its simplicity.

Naaman, captain of the host of Syria, went to the Israelitish prophet, Elisha, to be cured of his leprosy. As he was a great man with his master, he expected some special ceremony done for him. Imagine his surprise and wrath when bidden to wash in the River Jordan.

At first Naaman went away in a rage; such advice ill-befitted his ideas of his needs. If it were enough that he should bathe in a river, why in Jordan? "Are not Abana and Pharpar, rivers of Damascus, better than all the waters of Israel?" Why not wash in them and be clean? And Naaman turned and went away.

But his servants questioned him and said: "Had the prophet bid thee do some great thing, wouldst thou not have done it? How much rather then when he saith to thee 'wash and be clean'?" Then Naaman yielded and was made whole.

This story is a picture of our own ways. We despise the remedy that is simple, and we feel sure that, had it been some great thing, we should have found it easier to do. We are unwilling to accept simple, natural explanations of our difficulties. We feel so because we think so highly of ourselves. We forget that the greatest things are often the simplest, and, if the natural things are too hard for us to do, it is because we lack that true greatness which sees and welcomes directness.

If man understood his life better, he would cease to think of anything as an "accident" without a cause. He would know that nothing can occur to him that does not signify something to him in relation to his share in the plan of the Universe. He would understand that so simple a thing as whether or not he shall fall asleep as soon as he lies down to rest, or whether he shall find that "sleep has forsaken his eyes and slumber his eyelids," may be an experience of great importance to him.

Every incident of life is subject to law; yet many of the most important functions of the body are performed without any consciousness of their relation and dependence one upon another: as, for instance, breathing upon the circulation of the blood, which in turn depends upon the heart's pumping, and that upon the digestion, and that upon the food, and so on; the same is true of mental activities, and must be true of spiritual activities, for the same law runs through all of life. The wakefulness surely has some cause and some significance, else it had not been.

When something "goes wrong," we are forced to look into our case, and note the relation of one state of mind or body to other states. It is then, if ever, that we learn which is cause and which is effect; how mistakes result in pain and pain warns us of mistakes, and how one necessarily follows the other. If it were not for the pain that follows the violation of some natural law, man might go on in his unwise course until he had altogether destroyed his physical body.

It is the pain from the burn on the tiny hand that warns the infant not again to touch what he is told is "hot." If fire did not pain the body, we might be destroyed by flames without making any effort to escape. In fact, the chilliness and numbness of the African "sleeping sickness" often lead patients actually to burn off their hands or feet in the effort to get warm. It is quite possible that, if there were no pains in child-birth, women would bear children continually until they were themselves exhausted or their progeny overran one another. It is pain that tells us that a tooth is decayed, so that even toothache may be a blessing.

Therefore, if we are wise, instead of rebelling against pain, we should accept it gratefully as the helper and the possible preserver of our lives, and we should accept the wakefulness quietly as the sign of something that needs correction, or else as an opportunity for quiet thought and reflection.

When we have found what is wrong, and do our best to correct it, not only is the attention drawn from the pain to the remedy, but the effort to relieve it lessens the effect of the suffering.[5]

CHAPTER IX
SIMPLE CAUSES OF WAKEFULNESS

Where care lodges, sleep will never lie.
SHAKESPEARE.

W<small>E</small> all know the blessing of sleep, but it is hard to show the sufferer that wakefulness is useful.

Wakefulness always has some cause, and, if we truly wish to be cured of it, it will be well to seek the cause rather than to grumble at the wakefulness itself. It is not enough to know what is the matter, we must find out why it is the matter. To find the cause of any condition simplifies matters; it makes the course we must follow clearer. If the cause can be removed, we should bend all our energies to removing it; to paraphrase Stephen Pearl Andrews' saying—we are not to be subject to circumstances, but rather to make ourselves center-stances. But, if the matter be something over which we have no control, there are two courses open to us: the first is to accept the condition and adapt ourselves to it; the second is to devise some method by which we may gain control over it.

A childish story[6] will illustrate this:

Once there was a squirrel that did not like its home, and it used to scold and find fault with everything. Its papa squirrel had long gray whiskers, so he was wise. He said to the squirrel: "My dear, as you do not like your home, there are three sensible things you could do:

Leave it,
or Change it,
or Suit yourself to it.

Any one of these would help you in your trouble." But the little squirrel said, "Oh! I do not want to do any of those; I had rather sit on the branch of a tree and scold." "Well," said the papa squirrel, "if you must do that, whenever you want to scold, just go out on a branch and scold away at someone you do not know." The little squirrel blushed so much that he became a red squirrel, and you will notice that to this day red squirrels do just that thing.

Whatever course we pursue, we find something to do in connection with the underlying principle or cause; this *doing* prevents us from wasting energy and patience upon mere effects. That is an advantage, for any action relieves mental pain, and often relieves physical pain, too. The victim writhes not only in its effort to escape, but in the effort to express its feeling, to respond to the excited nerves, just as we dance about or hop up and down when we hit our finger with the hammer. We often hear people deplore that their suffering is increased because they can do nothing to remedy the trouble. We frequently exclaim, "It would be easier to bear, if only I could *do* something." A knowledge of what to do and how to do it always helps toward peace of mind.

When yellow fever was one of the "mysterious dispensations of Providence," men of science fought only its symptoms, with very indifferent success. The people in the district where the fever broke out were panic-stricken; those who could fled from the place; those who were compelled to remain went about in fear of their lives. Now that we believe that the bite of an infected mosquito is the once "mysterious dispensation," we no longer allow the infection to spread. Fear and unreason might have continued to treat outbreaks and epidemics of yellow fever for centuries to come without lasting advantage to the plague-ridden spots, but the knowledge of what to do and how to do it has made yellow fever a preventable evil. It has no terrors for an intelligent community.

So with wakefulness. If we find ourselves wakeful when we should be sleeping, the first thing to do is to find the reason.

Sometimes we cause our own sleeplessness unsuspectingly, but none the less deliberately, by the false requirements that we lay upon ourselves. People often say, "I could not go to sleep in a room like that." If there is time and opportunity to put the room in order, why do it; but, if not, we can resolve, as the boys say, to "forget it." Many a woman frets and disturbs herself continually by putting things in what she considers order, which things are no better for being rearranged and which generally cannot stay in order—endless pushing in of chairs and placing pamphlets or books with the little ones on top and the big ones at the bottom; a constant and wearisome struggle to keep all the shades in the house in a line. The labor of Sisyphus, who had forever to roll a great stone up a sand hill, would be restful compared with that. I knew a man once who would be entirely upset, and would upset all the people about him, if his stockings that came from the wash were not placed below those in the drawer so that they would surely be used in rotation.

Some persons cannot sleep after dawn if the light shines on their faces, yet are so possessed by the idea of order that they will not move the bed, disarrange the furniture to make a screen, or even sleep with their heads at the foot of the bed.

Another person insists always on being waked up by the last person to come home in order to be sure that the house was closed up. Still another cannot go to sleep till he has balanced up every cent of petty cash spent that day.

Many persons spend the most of their thought and exhaust themselves over things that are just as trivial and inconsequent as these; though they seem important to them. When anything has become such a habit, even though reasonable in itself, that you cannot sleep without it, you are paying too dear for it and it is time to change it. There is danger even in good habits—they may master us.

It may be that we have had some stimulating mental experience which has not yet relaxed its grip upon our attention. In such case even bodily weariness is apt to be forgotten, for, after all, every physical sensation is dependent upon some mental condition, whether fleeting or permanent. It is this interdependence of physical feeling and thought which makes it possible to recall emotions of pain or sorrow, of comfort or joy. The sight, the touch, or the smell of certain things will bring back sensations that once accompanied them, whether those sensations be painful or pleasant.

If the mind has been so stimulated that it cannot relax, there is little likelihood that sleep will come quickly, but we cannot relax by impatience. Tossing and turning will not quiet the mind; we must either accept the condition calmly and follow out the train of thought that has started or deliberately side-track the exciting cause. This may be done by setting up a counter activity in the mind along quieting lines. For instance, if one had walked the streets late on some such occasion as a New Year's Eve celebration in New York, and had become stimulated by the lights and the crowds, he might deliberately recall the most peaceful day in the country that it had been his fortune ever to know.

A typical scene of this sort is a warm Sunday in late spring, when all the usual activities of country life have ceased; the air is heavy with the scent of clover and field flowers, the apple blossoms, and the thousand odors of the fresh country field; the air moving so lazily that it scarcely stirs the trees; the cow chewing the meditative cud; the bees buzzing dreamily; the very horses, standing under the shed of the little white country church, whinnying softly to each other, as knowing that a spell of peace is over all, a spell that must not be broken; while from the church itself comes the drone of the preacher,—each little stir a part of the peace that broods over the day. Think of some such thing as that, recall it in all its details, and the chances are that the drowsiness induced at the time, whether one were of the congregation or a mere onlooker, will again steal over the eyelids and, before one is aware of any change, he is well on the way to the land of dreams.

In the same way if one has read an exciting book, or has seen a thrilling play, one may either live them over until the feelings exhaust themselves, because no longer new, or one may deliberately divert one's self from thinking of them and devote the attention to more soothing things. Either course removes all cause for impatience with the fact of wakefulness and leaves the mind quieted. This tends to drowsiness, even if it does not really induce sleep.

Sometimes it may help us if we rise and read some quieting book, not "a thriller." Such a volume as Thoreau's "Walden," or that more modern little volume, "Adventures in Contentment," by David Grayson, or we may repeat some soothing poem like Tennyson's "Sweet and Low," or Burroughs' "My Own Shall Come to Me" and similar verses.

Any of these will help to relax tension, and put us in a more restful frame of mind, and, as minds differ, so some persons will find books and verses of other sorts to have the desired effect upon them.

When we cannot sleep, to rise, throw back the bed-clothes so as to cool the bed, walk about the room, go to the window and fill the lungs with oxygen often tend to quiet the body and mind. We must learn to know our own needs and to find out each for himself what meets them. To "know thyself" is only the first step to control thyself.

CHAPTER X
"LIGHT" SLEEPERS

He sleeps well who knows not that he sleeps ill.
PUBLIUS SYRUS (42 B.C.).

SOMEONE may say that such things as stimulation of the mind are simple causes of wakefulness, and so easily overcome that it is hardly necessary to consider them; yet, simple as they are, they frequently make the wakeful one impatient. The more complex causes are really as easily dealt with as these simple ones, when once we have learned to control the mind. Take, for instance, the complaining "light sleeper" who cannot sleep if anybody else makes a noise, or if anything out of the ordinary occurs. He is in a steady state of apprehension lest something will happen to disturb his rest; and generally something does happen. A baby cries, a dog barks, a heavily-laden team lumbers by, an automobile honks, a locomotive shrieks, or a steamer whistles, and sleep forsakes him for the night.

He pronounces anathema on the offending cause; he pities himself for his sensitiveness, at the same time that he almost despises his fellows who are so "dead and unresponsive that they can sleep through such a racket" he suffers at the thought that he may get no more sleep, yet he enjoys the prospect of rehearsing to a sympathizing audience in the morning the tortures of such a delicate organization as his. This sort of sleeplessness is made up of so many contributing causes that it is difficult for any but the most perfectly honest man to decide what makes him so susceptible to noise. But it is undoubtedly true that some of these causes are due to fear, to training, and, most of all, to self-interest.

It is always difficult to make the super-sensitive person realize that his suffering is due chiefly to self-consideration and a desire to control others. It is an undue recognition of one's own claim upon the very circumstances of life that makes one offer so many surfaces which may be "hurt." We may be disturbed in our sleep by the ordinary pursuits of our fellows because we have an exaggerated idea of the importance of certain conditions that appeal to us and make for our comfort. We wish to sleep at a certain time, and we should like to regulate all our neighbors so that they, too, should suspend all activities at that same time. We accustom ourselves to quiet; and then insist that we cannot do without it.

There is a story told of a man working in a foundry who formed a part of two "shifts" of workmen and betweenwhiles slept for some hours in the foundry. When released from that strain, he found that he could not sleep at home because it was so quiet, and it became necessary for the members of his family to unite in making ringing, pounding noises to lull him to slumber.

It is a well-known fact that those who live near the cataracts of the Nile cannot sleep if they get beyond the sound of the pounding. Soldiers, who are wearied after a hard day's march or fighting, will sleep soundly beside twenty-four pounder guns steadily firing; or even sleep on the march, their legs moving mechanically though their senses are steeped in sleep.

Country people coming to the city are kept awake by the unusual street noises, while city-dwellers, accustomed to the roar of elevated or subway trains, are unable to sleep in the country because of the intense silence which Nature's noises often emphasize.

Unreflecting man is a creature of habit: if any change occurs in his routine, he finds it difficult to adapt himself to it. He seldom comes to understand that it is chiefly insistence upon his own needs as apart from the needs or interests of others that makes him require certain conditions for sleeping. In either case the cause of wakefulness is easily found; but nobody other than the individual most concerned can remove it.

If we are living in selfish disharmony with our fellows; if we are indulging feelings of envy, malice, uncharitableness or hatred towards those about us, we are not likely to sleep refreshingly. All such emotions do more harm to the one who feels them than to those against whom they are directed. They may undermine the health, destroy the mental poise, and blot out the sense of kinship with mankind. The Hebrews understood that so well that he who would offer a sacrifice is reminded that, if he have aught against his brother, he must leave his gift at the altar and make his peace before he can offer an acceptable sacrifice to God.

If wakefulness be the result of impatience with our brother, there is only one cure for it: that is, to replace it with loving patience. It is the lack of love, or the possession of very narrow love, that causes us pain in our relations with other people.

CHAPTER XI
THE GIFTS OF WAKEFULNESS

"B UT," you say, "I am not full of uncharitableness towards my fellows and I am willing they should live their own lives; I am greatly worried about my own affairs and all my cares come trooping back to me as soon as I lie down. I cannot sleep for worry." Yes; but is not that only another form of selfishness? A subtle form, but none the less disturbing. Moreover, it is shortsighted, as is all selfishness, for it is a boomerang. If the worry is about business, we shall need a clear brain and a steady nerve to face the condition that is causing the uneasiness; and worry at night will not give us these. On the contrary, it will destroy what remnant of poise we may have.

The solution of trouble is not found in worry. Just recall how often you have said yourself, or heard somebody say, "After all my worrying it came out all right; it is strange that I never once thought of that way." Worry prevents clear thinking, or, indeed, thinking of any sort. We go around and around in a circle until we grow giddy and faint with apprehension, while all the time we might have peace if we but looked at life aright, to see that, in the words of the old Book, "it is all very good." When a mechanic is putting a machine together and finds that the parts do not fit, that they do not "go right" or harmonize, he will reach one of two conclusions. Either the maker did not know his business, and so did not make the parts to fit, or else he, himself, is putting them together in the wrong way. If he wants to put that machine together so that it will work well, he will look into the matter carefully, examining each part, all the time keeping in his mind a conception of the complete machine. He will probably find that he has been trying to fit two unrelated parts together, or has reversed their position, misunderstood or only partially understood their uses, or has done something through carelessness that may easily be corrected. Of course, if he is a stupid or foolish workman, and not a skilled mechanic, he may persist in his wrong course and fail to get the machine into working order. But that is not the fault of the maker, nor does it prove that the machine would not do perfect work if it were rightly understood and intelligently controlled. So it is with the Cosmos, the orderly world, which will go right for us if we do our part right.

The first step towards knowing how to get anything is to have a clear idea of what it is that we want; for development is not thrust upon us, nor dropped upon us by our parents. It is desire that creates function; the creature that wants to swim is the creature that learns to swim; the bird that does not want to fly will lose the power; before we can rise higher, we must look higher.

"When the ideal once alights in our streets," says Edward Carpenter, "we may go home to supper in peace, the rest will be seen to." But, if we enjoy worry as the countryman's wife "enjoys poor health," we shall continue to have it, for we always get what we most want, if we set about it in the right way. And if we do not want worry, we need not worry. If the trouble is unavoidable or unchangeable, it were wise to use our powers to adjust ourselves to the inevitable. If it be a curable trouble, the only thing is to discover or devise a cure. As soon as we start to work we cease to worry, because worry and effective activity cannot exist at the same time. Man, at least, is such a creature that any real action looking towards a definite end brings him pleasure; and, though the action may have been stimulated by pain, yet the pleasure he finds in the action mitigates, if it does not destroy, the pain.

If the original cause for the worry lies in our own ignorance, selfishness, or thoughtlessness, the anxiety may teach us to repair the ill so that we may not have to get the same lesson again. But worrying will teach us less than a cheerful acceptance of the facts—or than that courage which says,

> "And still the menace of the years
> Finds and shall find me unafraid"—

and one of the best aids to cheerfulness is sound, refreshing sleep. If we should put off all worrying until the morning, there would be very little worrying done by the normal, healthy person, for, after a good night's sleep and in the clear light of day, things look much better than they did in the darkness and solitude of the night, with mind and body worn from the activities of the day.

If we feel that our affairs are too important to be left to the care of the Providence that keepeth Israel, and slumbers not nor sleeps, then at least we may wait until morning to give our attention to them. It is unfair to bring exhausted faculties to bear upon matters of so great weight. If our troubles can be helped by worrying, we should worry when we are in the best possible trim. To do less were to underestimate their importance and to prove that, anyway, they are not worth losing sleep over.

But there is still another way of looking at wakefulness, when we cannot trace the cause of it. It may be the time sent to us by the Spirit for quiet thought. The ancients believed that God spoke in visions of the night. We may not always be able to sleep, but we can always lie in the arms of our Great Mother Nature. There is a real philosophy as well as devotion in the old prayer we teach our children, "Now I lay me down to sleep." A still older form of the almost instinctive recognition of the fact that sleeping is but intrusting ourselves to the Universal love was, "He committed himself to God in sleep." Like sleep, a wakeful night may be a growing time. It affords the quiet, the time, the seclusion to think over the meanings of things, or even to seek the cause of the wakefulness itself. For that is the first thing to do if we find ourselves wakeful; if the cause be so obscure that we cannot find it, then the best thing to do is to accept the fact.

Either we do not need the sleep we are seeking,—the reclining position being all the *rest* the body needs,—or else we do need the wakefulness to teach us something that we can learn or will learn in no other way. It is a time when, free from the watchful eyes of those who love us, or those who do not love us, we need not fear to look at ourselves, our motives, our relations to our fellows.

It may be only at such a time that we can feel the closeness of the tie that binds all mankind, only in such a time that a life-giving sense of oneness can renew life and joy. Some persons are so acutely conscious of the surge around them during the day that it is difficult, if not impossible, for them to get any large view of it. They are so beset and bewildered by each little detail of life that they cannot see any relation among things as a whole, cannot "see the wood for the trees." Or, it may be that a lack of poise, a false estimate of the relations of things, makes them find "their own affairs" so interesting or exhausting that the observing mind gets no large or deep impressions to be added to the sum of the knowledge the inner self possesses.

For either of these classes the wakeful night may prove more restful and helpful than hours of sleep. It may be made to bring a breadth of view that will lift one out of the narrow limits in which daily life is passed. It may do as much as this for any of us, and, if we reject the receptive mood, and insist upon objecting to the wakefulness, we may thereby deprive ourselves of some of the most illuminating experiences.

Someone has said: "Sleep, like drink, may drown our sorrows, yet it also drowns our joys. What could we not accomplish if we did not require sleep?" It may be comforting to think of this when we are lying awake, that at least we are wasting no time. The gift of wakefulness is often as desirable as is the gift of sleep, and, if we welcome the one as what must be—with as much cheerfulness as the other—each will bring us equal blessings. It often happens that what we regard as evil is but Life's left hand outstretched with a gift whose use we did not recognize when presented by her right hand.

CHAPTER XII
THE PURPOSE OF SLEEP

Sleep is a life giver as well as a life saver.
WILLARD MOYER.

B UT none of these things lessens the benefits of real sleep, nor are they intended to show that sleep is unnecessary, for although it may be true, as Dr. Charles Brodie Patterson says in "The New Heaven and the New Earth," that man will some day get along without sleep, no one is yet able to do that.

Although our troubles make us lose sleep, we could lose all or nearly all our troubles if we got natural sleep. Forgetfulness of daily frets, of the wear and tear of contact with the sharp edges of our own temper and the temper of others—these are the things that sleep blots out. "Go to sleep," says Mother Nature, "and forget your troubles." And to blot them out even for a time means surcease of sorrow and worry for that time at least, and a new way of looking at them when we have awakened. That is what sleep is for. It is the use of it.

Pat took Mike to church for the first time, and, when the ceremony was over, he said, "Well, Mike, what do you think uv it?" "Think uv it, Pat? The candles, the bowings, the incinse, and the garmints,—it do bate the divil."

"Sure," replied Pat, "thot's the intintion." And so it is the intention of sleep to "beat the devil" of unrest and dissatisfaction. Nothing makes us feel better than a good night's sleep. It soothes the aching muscles, quiets the jangling nerves, brushes away the cobwebs of the mind, and leaves us rested and refreshed, strong to meet the events of the new day.

It is after a bad night that we rise oppressed with fear for what the day may bring us; overwhelmed in advance with shadowings of evil. This, in itself, makes us unequal to the demands of the day. If any seeming strain is put upon us that day, we are apt to make errors in meeting it; if we find anyone has failed to do just what seemed to us best, we upbraid him roundly and unlovingly, making him and ourselves unhappy.

At the close of such a spoiled day, when we review its happenings, we say: "I knew this morning that this would be an unlucky day. I felt it as soon as I got up." But we may not realize that that very attitude of fear and apprehension may have caused all that we call ill-luck. Remember this, then, lest the one bad day should spoil another night.

Often after a night of sound, wholesome, refreshing sleep we are surprised to find that what looked like a mountain at midnight is now scarcely a hillock. We find that we can see around it on all sides, and the prospect of surmounting that difficulty fills us with peculiar delight. We are no longer apprehensive of anything. The things we see in our work in the world are no more terrible than what we see in that unknown world which we enter nightly through the gate of sleep. We long to pass that gate, yet we know nothing of where we go, how far we travel, or by what means we come back.

If we can trust Life for what the night brings, we can trust it further and gladly accept what the day brings. We feel this, even if we are not conscious of it, and after a good sleep (this is what sleep is for), we accept it much as the child accepts his mother's care.

A little boy was riding in a trolley car with his parents and persisted in standing up, to the terror of his mother, who begged him to sit down lest he get hurt.

Turning to his father he whispered, as he reluctantly took his seat, "What a 'fraid-cat mother is." "Oh, well!" replied his father, "she is nervous, but you know she has to take care of her little boy." "Yes," said the child, "that's what she is for." So that is what sleep is for—to take care of us, but we cannot compel sleep; and the advantage of recognizing the possible gifts of wakefulness is that we thus get around to the frame of mind where we drop into natural sleep. Impatience not only delays the coming of sleep, but it robs us of any benefit we might receive from lying peacefully in the dark.

CHAPTER XIII
THE SLEEP OF THE INVALID

Sleep, O gentle Sleep,
    Nature's soft nurse—

                  SHAKESPEARE.

WE should not think that, because we are ill, it is natural that we should not sleep. The invalid needs more and better sleep than the robust person—and the invalid can have it.

It is true that, as more and better sleep comes, the invalid will cease to be an invalid—at least that is the beginning of the end of invalidism. For Nature provides sleep as the "balm of hurt minds"—a cure for body or mind that needs restoring.

In the case of severe illness the physician in charge feels relieved when he learns that his patient is sleeping well. The professional idea of sleep is that nutrition goes on most perfectly during sleeping hours; that is, that Nature repairs all the waste that results from the use of brain and muscle during our waking hours. The more prolonged and undisturbed the sleep is, the more opportunity Nature has to make good the extra demands made upon the system by disease. It opens the way for the "Vis Medicatrix Naturæ"—the healing power of Life.

Take, for example, the fever patient. Anyone who has watched beside a loved one slowly consuming, with the fever raging in his blood, will remember the sigh of relief that has gone up from physician and nurse when the patient falls into a natural sleep after the turn of things. During dreadful nights and anxious days we wait breathlessly for the "crisis"; we hang upon the physician's word, scan his face for every fleeting expression, because we may be deceived by the disease, but his practiced eye should know. But we do not need his assurance when the moaning and restlessness pass, when the stertorous breathing quiets, when the skin becomes moist, and the gentle, regular breathing tells us that natural sleep has come. If we can be spared, we go out under the stars and, whether Christian or pagan, up from the depths of our souls wells a prayer of thankfulness to "whatever gods there be" for the incomparable blessing of sleep. We feel as if we could "go softly all our days" before the powers who have decreed that sleep shall gently steep the eyelids of the one we love.

Nourishment, in the form of food, is desirable, but more important still is the sleep when Nature busies herself building new tissue and blood to make good the ravages of fever's siege. We are careful to keep even good news from the patient, if we have cause to fear that it will prove too stimulating, and everything depressing or alarming is absolutely withheld, because sleep is the paramount need of the depleted body.

We all recognize the value of sleep to the person just past the crisis of a severe illness, and the next thing to learn is that to the person invalided through some less active cause, it is as necessary, and that it may be had.

It may seem an extravagant statement to say that the invalid should be able to summon sleep at will even better than an active, healthy person. But we may see the truth of this statement if we accept Dr. Edward Binns' assurance that "in no sense can fatigue be said to be the cause of sleep," so that the usual claim that the sick do not get an opportunity to weary themselves, and so cannot expect sound sleep, cannot be accounted a reason for sleeplessness of the invalid.

To be sure, lying abed is not always restful. A friend of mine was kept in bed for some weeks by a broken ankle. It was necessary to remain in the one position day and night, which so wore upon her nervous organization that she grew restless and "lost" much sleep. In this condition, she said the hardest thing to bear was the well-meant congratulations of her friends that at least she was "getting a much-needed rest." But the real reason why an invalid should learn to sleep at will is because sleep alone can do what Macbeth asks of the physician:

> "Canst thou not minister to a mind diseased,
> Pluck from the memory a rooted sorrow,
> Raze out the written troubles of the brain,
> And with some sweet oblivious antidote
> Cleanse the stuff'd bosom of that perilous stuff
> Which weighs upon the heart?"

Yes, sleep can do this; and illness has need of just such comfort. The enforced idleness leads to much reflection and the nervous system is then ill-adapted to endure emotional strain. If pain be added there is still greater need for sleep. Nor is pain absolutely hostile to sleep: the writer can often go to sleep while the dentist is drilling and filling his teeth, and Dr. J. Howard Reed says that this is not very uncommon.

Pain is Nature's strong protest against overstimulation or overexertion and the exhaustion which it occasions is itself conducive to sleep. It would be better for us to heed that protest and use our intelligence to secure sound, refreshing sleep, that Nature might perfect her cures.

CHAPTER XIV
THE SLEEPLESSNESS OF PAIN

He kisses brows that ache from earthly care;
He soothes to peace the indignant souls of slaves.
EDGAR FAWCETT.

SOMETIMES we are kept awake by pain. Some persons suffer pain that has no remission, except the temporary deadness that comes from nervous exhaustion—and sleep.

But sometimes the hardest torture is the thought that the pain is unnecessary or useless. I went once to visit a friend, whom I found suffering from the worst abscesses on the back of the neck that I ever saw, so frightful that the sight of them made me, who am a strong man, feel faint. I asked sympathetically what was the matter. "Oh," he said, "I'm getting some experience." That consciousness that such pain was useful helped to make the agony less unendurable. In fact, though he did not see it all then, he was getting just what he and those about him needed. He was a vigorous man, who took to rural work in a place where the food was excellent; he was naturally gluttonous and overate, hence the boils. This he learned; and also how to bear pain.

There are ways of bearing pain more easily. We must consider the pain philosophically, and treat it from all three sides—the bodily, the intellectual, and the spiritual.

However advanced we may be, it is foolish to deny that, in common with the rest of mankind, we are more or less in what Paul called the bonds of the flesh. To try to treat an aching tooth without physical means is like trying to grow a new leg instead of getting an artificial one. There was a stage in man's Pre-Adamite progress from the amœba when, like the crab, he could grow new legs. Possibly, by discarding all other faculties, men might again be able to grow new legs: but it would not pay.

A man who makes hammers may at one time have made his own files, had a shop for that. But, as trades became specialized, he found it better and cheaper to buy his files. Perhaps the supply is suddenly cut off. Now he could reassemble from the scrap-heap the file machinery and make files again, but it would be at the cost of putting so much time and energy into that branch as to paralyze the hammer factory.

So, Nature found that men rarely lost their legs and that it was more economical to divert the organization and the energy that reproduced legs into the brain, which enables men to supply themselves and their fellows, when occasion arises, with artificial legs. Accordingly we have lost much of the power of automatic self-healing and have gained much power of deliberate self-healing.

While distrusting crutches and drugs, therefore, because we see the immediate effect of them, but cannot know the remote effects of them, we cannot refuse a hot-water bottle or an anæsthetic when the pain, the symptom of the disorder, becomes dangerous in itself. The fever of typhoid represents a battle within which must be fought out to a conclusion—successful or not. But, when the patient is in danger of dying from the high temperature, it is no inconsistency for a mental or spiritual healer to cool the room or sponge the patient with alcohol.

Before we resort to the dentist for the aching tooth, we may reduce the inflammation by abstaining from food and starving the blood corpuscles, which hasten to the diseased part, until, perhaps, they feed upon the weaker and obnoxious tissues. This abstinence will go far toward removing the restlessness that is so torturing an accompaniment of the pain. These are the physical remedies.

The mental ones consist mainly in trying to isolate the aching member, to realize that it is the tooth, not you, that aches, and to watch it as if it were a separate person. A little boy was asked how he felt after a feast of green apples. "I have a pain in the middle of my stomach," he said, "but the rest of me feels fine." A further mental remedy is to send to that separated part, the nerve, the assurance that you have already its message, which is that there is inflammation in the tooth and that you will attend to it as speedily as possible. The nerve gets tired, as it were, of repeating a message that gets no attention just as it gets tired of reporting the ticking of a clock so that we become unconscious of it; although, if we suspected that it was the knocking of a burglar's tool, we should be kept awake by it night after night.

And we must not complain. The Japanese think it rude to complain. If you are miserable, why make others miserable, too? Better not even let it be known, if you can help it without creating unpleasantness, that you suffer. To solicit sympathy is weakening and the constant inquiry, "How are you now?" concentrates your attention on yourself and on your feelings. If we complained to everyone of the ticking clock, we would never forget it; it would become less and less endurable.

The spiritual treatment is harder to make clear. It is the unwillingness to have pain that makes it hard to bear. To illustrate again from the dentist, because that experience is still common to nearly everyone: We go to the operating chair, not gladly, but willingly, believing that it is wise and necessary and we bear the pain without complaining, knowing that it is the common lot of man. But suppose you were seized, strapped into the chair, and then your teeth were drilled and sawed to no good purpose, how much more frightful would be the pain. That would be because you believed it to be unnecessary and useless. It would be quite different if you trusted the operator. We must realize, then, that, if there is a controlling and benevolent Power in the Universe, which we all, rightly or wrongly, believe in our hearts, we never can have any pain that is useless or needless to ourselves, or to others, our other selves.

We may not see it at the time, but, if we look for it, we usually shall see it. While writing this the author was attacked with a violent toothache: he had exercised ordinary prudence in attending to his teeth, so that it did not seem as if the pain were needed to teach care. But when the toothache came he remembered that, seldom having pain himself, that subject had been overlooked among the many chapters of the book. That was a reason; but, notwithstanding the efforts of an excellent dentist, the torture continued. Why?

Why, that he might try these things; and he did practice them so as to lose no sleep. In addition he concluded that it was needful just then that he should feel just such pain in order to revive his sympathy and patience with those whose harassed nerves account for so much of their unreasonableness.

With that sense, that one is in a manner suffering for men, comes something of the exaltation of the martyr, even with prosaic toothache. With that certainly disappears all impatience with the pain.

Perhaps he will be accounted superstitious in adding that, when these lessons were learned, the dentist found the trouble and the pain melted away. But he has had exactly similar experiences before: a new lesson or a renewal of it was needed. When the pain was no longer necessary it ceased. Why should it continue?

SWEET AND LOW

Sweet and low, sweet and low,
    Wind of the western sea;
Low, low, breathe and blow,
    Wind of the western sea!
Over the rolling waters go,
Come from the dying moon, and blow,
    Blow him again to me;
      While my little one,
      While my pretty one,
        Sleeps.

Sleep and rest, sleep and rest;
    Father will come to thee soon.
Rest, rest on Mother's breast;
    Father will come to thee soon.
Father will come to his babe in the nest,—
Silver sails all out of the west
    Under the silver moon!
      Sleep, my little one;
      Sleep my pretty one,
        Sleep.
TENNYSON.

CHAPTER XV
OPIATES

O NE of the most common signs of something at fault either with the body or the mind is headache. Now headache, like wakefulness or nervousness, so often associated with headache, is an effect of some error, not a cause of it, and the wise sufferer will seek the cause even before he treats the effect.

We call ourselves the most enlightened nation of the earth to-day, and it is true that a little knowledge has been more generally diffused among our people than among other peoples of the world. But we should not forget that "a little knowledge is a dangerous thing" largely because a little knowledge frequently proves to be no real knowledge at all. For example, the "little knowledge" generally possessed in regard to opiates.

Coal-tar was once a waste product, but toward the end of the last century a German chemist discovered that from it could be derived a drug, acetanilid, which would greatly lower temperature in fever. This discovery was hailed as a boon to humanity, and many other by-products of coal-tar were soon placed on the market, and regarded as of equal value with acetanilid. Physicians used them for a time without questioning, and the people took to them gladly. Wherever there was a persistent headache, some one of the coal-tar products was used, and "headache powders" multiplied.

But a little further knowledge led physicians to question the expediency of using acetanilid, phenacetin, antipyrin, or any of the coal-tar preparations in other than exceptional cases. Heart-failure and other dangerous results so frequently followed their use that the wisdom of using them at all became doubtful. As our knowledge increases, we are likely to find both the wisdom and necessity entirely disappearing.

In the meantime, those who have heard that temporary relief from pain may be had by using these drugs will go on using them, often in patent medicines, ignorant of what these nostrums contain, and the number of deaths resulting from their use continues to increase. The only way to protect such people from the result of their little knowledge, which is really ignorance, is by making it illegal to sell these drugs, except by prescription from a physician, who, in turn, should be held responsible for results.

This is, of course, an interference with the individual's right to do as seemeth best to him, and to get his experience in his own way. Herbert Spencer says, "The ultimate result of shielding men from the effects of folly is to fill the world with fools." But it is the same sort of interference that makes us hold a man by main force from throwing himself on the track before an approaching train, and not the sort that would forcibly put an overcoat on him when he did not care to wear it. One may be no more justifiable than the other, but it seems more excusable.

All sleeping doses are to be viewed with distrust; most of them contain opium or morphine, some still more deadly drugs: Nature "sets up a tolerance" for them so that, to obtain the effect, the dose must be increased, until, if the sufferer does not retreat in time, an almost incurable drug habit is formed, often more terrible than the liquor habit, which it sometimes supplants. Nor do they bring true sleep.

R. Clarke Newton, in his treatise on "Opium and Alcohol," says "Sleeplessness means not merely unrest, but starvation of the cerebrum. The only cause for regret in these cases is that the blunder should ever be committed of supposing that a stupefying drug which throws the brain into a condition that mimics and burlesques sleep can do good. It is deceptive to give narcotics in a case of this type. The stupor simply masks the danger. Better far let the sleepless patient exhaust himself than stupefy him. Chloral, bromides, and the rest of the poisons that produce a semblance of sleep are so many snares in such cases. Sleeplessness is a malady of the most formidable character, but it is not to be treated by intoxicating the organ upon which the stress of the trouble falls." The late Dr. Alonzo Clark, who for years stood at the head of his profession as a consulting physician in New York City, is quoted as saying, "All curative agents, so called, are poisons, and, as a consequence, every dose diminishes the patient's vitality." I doubt whether this view of drugs would be seriously contested by any of his professional brethren of good standing.

The venerable Professor Joseph M. Smith, M.D., said: "All medicines which enter the circulation poison the blood in the same manner as do the poisons that produce the disease. Drugs do not cure disease." John Bigelow, in the "Mystery of Sleep" (p. 190), adds: "With drug-poisons should be classed nearly, if not quite, all fermented drinks—the most costly part of some people's diet who indulge in them at all—coffee, tea, tobacco, spices, and most of the constantly multiplying tonics and condiments of the table. All of them have a tendency, directly or indirectly, to discourage or impair sleep, and, as such, are 'hostes humani generis' (enemies of the human race). Their interference with sleep, though perhaps the most serious, is very far from being their only pathogenetic influence."

Mr. Bigelow then cites from Jahr's "Manual of Medicine" the fearful disturbances of sleep caused by fifteen drugs, all taken as samples from the list in their order under the single letter "A." Contrary to the general belief, sleeplessness is more often a consequence of insanity than a cause of it. (See Appendix A.)

CHAPTER XVI
DEVICES FOR GOING TO SLEEP

Southey, in "The Doctor," thus summarizes some of the chief devices to attain sleep by monotony: "I listened to the river and to the ticking of my watch; I thought of all sleepy sounds and of all soporific things—the flow of water, the humming of bees, the motion of a boat, the waving of a field of corn, the nodding of a mandarin's head on the chimney-piece, a horse in a mill, the opera, Mr. Humdrum's conversations, Mr. Proser's poems, Mr. Laxative's speeches, Mr. Lengthy's sermons. I tried the device of my own childhood, and fancied that the bed rushed with me round and round. At length Morpheus reminded me of Dr. Torpedo's Divinity Lectures, where the voice, the manner, the matter, even the very atmosphere and the streaming candle-light, were all alike soporific; when he who, by strong effort, lifted up his head and forced open the reluctant eyes, never failed to see all around him asleep. Lettuces, cowslip wine, poppy syrup, mandragora, hop pillows, spider's web pills, and the whole tribe of narcotics would have failed—but this was irresistible; and thus twenty years after date, I found benefit from having attended the course."

FREQUENT impressions on the mind, or calls on the attention, tend to make us sleepy; thus looking at pictures, the attempt to study, driving in a carriage. In extreme cases this is very marked. A boy named Caspar Hauser was shut up alone in a gloomy little room until he was about eighteen years old; then he was brought to Nürnberg and abandoned in the street; this was in 1828. He was to all intents a baby and could not walk, nor speak, nor see clearly, as he had never known any of the common objects of life—men or animals or plants, or the moon or sun or even the sky.

He would go to sleep instantly on being taken outside the house, because the number of new sensations instantly tired his consciousness.

For the same reason that the consciousness is quickly exhausted, many old or delicate persons readily fall asleep. Marie de Manacéïne says that Moivre, the French mathematician, used to sleep twenty hours a day during his old age, leaving only four for science and the other occupations of life.

Monotony naturally fatigues consciousness and is often successfully used to produce sleep; the regular dropping of water, the sound of a brook will put those to sleep whom it does not make nervous. Lullabies and slumber songs and dull lectures all come under the same head of devices to tire the consciousness.

Narcotic drugs do not weary consciousness; they simply destroy it. They stupefy us instead of inducing sleep. Those who would wisely learn about this by experiments upon others rather than upon themselves, will find it all in the article by Ringer and Sainsbury on "Sedatives" in Tuke's "Dictionary of Psychological Medicine." It is enough for us to be assured that narcotic sleep is less like real sleep than the hibernation of the animal is like repose. (But see "Remedies" in Appendix A.)

Henry Ward Beecher used to get up when he was sleepless and take a cold bath, a good device for a full-blooded, vigorous person: but a weak person would not "react" and get warm again. For such an one it would be better to sponge off and restore the circulation by rubbing. Some physicians have prescribed, with good success, blood-warm baths, beginning at a temperature of about 98 and heated up to 110 or 115 Fahrenheit. When the moisture has been absorbed by wrapping one's self in a blanket, throw it off and get quickly into a warm bed. Mark Twain used to get to sleep by lying down on the bathroom floor after the bath.

Some, when other means fail, find it effective to place a cold-water bag at the back of the neck, or to rub the feet with a rough towel: with others, a hot-water bottle at the back of the neck works better. A warm footbath helps some persons. At the sanitariums they sponge with warm water, rub with wet salt, gently sponge it off, and dry the body—all of which helps the blood to the surface. It is always well to see that the bowels are emptied. Only trial and judgment will show whether any of these will effect a cure: they all aim at the same mark, to abstract the blood from the brain.

That drinking milk produces sleep in some persons may probably be due to the lactic acid in the milk, which is a soporific like morphine. Perhaps its use is to help young animals to the long sleeps they need.

Willard Moyer, in an entertaining essay, tells us that it is often advisable for the stomach to have sufficient work for the blood to do so as to call it from the brain. This does not mean that a meal that will overload the stomach is a cure for insomnia, but that something light, such as a cup of warm milk and a cracker, may often "send one comfortably to sleep like a drowsy kitten or a well-fed baby." A. Fleming, following Durham, the author of the "Psychology of Sleep," showed that to deprive the brain of blood by pressing the carotid arteries for thirty seconds brought immediate and deep sleep, but it only continued while all pulsation of these arteries is stopped.[7]

It has been found by cruel experiments on young puppies that sleep is more necessary to them than food, as they die after being kept awake four or five days, but may live ten or fifteen days without food. They easily go to sleep when their heads are level with their bodies, and they will not go to sleep with their heads lower than their bodies: of course, the raised head drains some blood out of the brain.

This is the reason that heat or extreme cold, both of which bring the blood to the surface and drain it away from the brain, will often produce sleep. That is why the cowboy likes to sleep with his feet to the fire. On the other hand, the demand on the heart of cold hands or feet for more blood to keep them warm may make the heart pump so strongly that it sends more blood to the brain and keeps one awake. So also joy, anger, or anxiety cause a flow of blood to the brain and hinder sleep.

Becker and Schuller have treated insomnia by wrapping the entire body in wet sheets and also by applying cold compresses to the head. This last device is used by students, with doubtful success, "to keep the brain cool"; it is sometimes affected because it looks like working hard. Sometimes an ice cap, a double rubber cap filled with cold water, will bring sleep.

The Russian nobles used to make servants scratch their heels for a long time; our ladies have their hair brushed; and A. H. Savage-Landor says that Corean mothers put their babies to sleep by scratching them gently on the stomach. I have tried this rubbing, rather than scratching, with great success. Spanish women rub the children's upper spine to put them to sleep. Light exercise before lying down is often a good expedient.

Sometimes a pillow of heated hops or of balsam pine needles will induce sleep. To change the hour of going to bed occasionally, yielding to apparently untimely drowsiness, often helps, as it accustoms us to gain sleep at irregular times.

To "relax," to let the muscles become perfectly loose, is an art, though it should be natural to one going to sleep. Mrs. Richard Hovey recommends shaking the fingers, letting them hang loose like a bunch of strings of beads, and extending the movement to the wrist, arms, feet, and legs. This is the best form of calisthenic exercise for sleeplessness. It aids us in getting limp so as to lie at ease.

CHAPTER XVII
MORE DEVICES FOR GOING TO SLEEP

Oh Sleep! it is a gentle thing,
Beloved from pole to pole.

COLERIDGE.

I F life be a succession of ideas, says Dr. Binns, then sleep is the interval; "consequently, we may say that sleep is the art of escaping reflection." If one could follow the Chinese advice, divest the mind of all unpleasant images, "the secret of sleep at will," Dr. Binns thinks, "would be in the possession of all men." This accords in its essence with the very modern theory of Dr. Henry Hubbard Foster of Cornell University, that sleep results from the absence of stimulations. It is conceivable that things that stimulate, or rouse us, may come from inside as well as from outside. A sudden thought, a new, delightful, or horrible mental picture will arouse us and send sleep flying as effectually as a sudden noise or an exciting commotion from without.

We might amend the Chinese advice thus: put out of the mind all images, pleasant or unpleasant, or, as Dr. Gardner puts it, "bring the mind to a single sensation." It has long been known that monotony will induce sleep. Not merely the monotony of silence, but sometimes even the monotony of great noise, such as the ceaseless firing of heavy guns which have lulled the wearied soldiers into rest. There is a sleepy sound in "The distant boom of a random gun which the foe was sullenly firing." It is the sudden, irregular noise which disturbs. If anyone listens for several hours to soft, flowing music, he will have great difficulty in keeping awake, no matter how great a lover of music he may be, particularly if he has to sit in the same position all the time. Let a musical number with strongly marked staccato movement be introduced, let the drum throb loud at intervals, the horns blare, then the sleeper will awake and find renewed enjoyment, not because he loves noise, but because the monotony has been broken. The mind has responded to the new stimulus.

Professor Boris Sidis, of the Harvard Physiological Laboratory, says that "the fundamental conditions of sleep are monotony and limitation of voluntary movements. Sleep," adds Sidis, is not so much due to cutting off impressions through the senses, be they intense or faint, as to the monotony of the "impressions that reduced the organism to the passive state which we experience in sleep." In other words, monotony has such a benumbing, deadening effect upon the mind that sleep naturally ensues.

Although Binns did not know Foster's and Sidis' modern views, yet accepting Gardner's theory of "bringing the mind to a single sensation," he worked out a plan for inducing sleep which he said nearly always succeeded. During his long practice he had known of only two instances where it failed when faithfully and intelligently tried.

The method is simple, yet it includes putting out of the mind all images pleasant or unpleasant, and restricting voluntary movements. It is this: "Turn on the right side, place the head comfortably on the pillow, let the head fall naturally, using the pillow only to support the neck, slightly close the lips,—though this is not absolutely essential,—take full inspiration through the nostrils, drawing in as much air as possible, then leave the lungs to their own action, neither hastening nor checking exhalation. Think of the breath as passing from the nostrils in one continuous stream, and, the very instant the person so conceives, consciousness and memory depart, the muscles relax, the breath comes regularly, he no longer wakes but sleeps. It is all the effort of but a moment."

Another method in common use is counting up to a hundred on an imaginary string of beads. Often one will have lost consciousness before the hundredth bead is reached, but sometimes they have to be counted over and over, and sometimes the plan fails altogether. The immediate reason for this is undoubtedly that we have not brought the mind to a single sensation, nor succeeded in cutting off the impressions that come through the senses.

Everybody has at some time used some such device for inducing sleep to visit him. The practice of imagining sheep jumping over a gate and counting them as they go is but another way of bringing the mind to a single sensation, of deliberately securing monotony and shutting out all stimuli, as scientific men call the various causes that arouse sensation in us. Such simple devices are never harmful, and are so frequently followed by sleep that they continue from generation to generation.

If the impressions received through the channels of sense cannot or will not be shut off, it is useless to continue counting beads or sheep, or seeing a stream of breath. It becomes necessary to discover what it is that is back of the stimulation—what impression is so vivid and so insistent that it will not down. As Frederick Palmer says in his delightful book, "The Vagabond," we should "take a good look at a thing before we run away from it."

CHAPTER XVIII
STILL FURTHER DEVICES

The sleep of a laboring man is sweet.
Ecclesiastes.

"THE Witchery of Sleep" records for us some interesting mechanical devices for inducing sleep, more common in Europe than in this country. Their inventors hope to perfect them so that they may take the place of drugs and "sleeping potions." This is an end devoutly to be wished by all who know the steady increase of the "drug habit." Among these sleep-inducing instruments the newest is the "vibrating coronet." This coronet has three metal bands which encircle the head and two strips extending to the eyelids. By means of a spring these strips vibrate the eyelid gently and induce drowsiness. All the mechanical devices are constructed on the plan of inducing eye-weariness, whether by vibration or by fixity. Either effect is in accordance with the modern theories of sleep. Sleep may be induced by monotony also of sounds; by concentration either of the attention or the hearing on one point, or by more numerous impressions than the eye can comfortably receive; thus, when riding in a train, the succession of views will often induce sleepiness.

The "Alouette," a collection of little mirrors attached to the ebony panels of a box, is so placed that a ray of light falls on the mirrors in such a way as to fatigue the eye of the beholder. Both this and the "Fascinator," a highly polished nickel ball attached to a flexible wire depending from a metal band similar to the "Coronet," work on the plan of concentrating the vision. In a similar way a light-house or a miniature flashlight, with its appearing and disappearing light, induces drowsiness, possibly hypnotic, through incessant change. It is needless to say that these devices might be injurious to the sight and certainly would not work where the cause of sleeplessness is eyestrain. That is a case for the oculist.

But when it is impossible to obtain mechanical devices, there are many simple schemes of inducing sleep. Any light work, mental or physical, is helpful. To start writing letters, particularly if one is not fond of letter-writing, will sometimes induce sleepiness very quickly. Sorting and arranging old papers will have the same effect, unless one is of a nature to find such an occupation exciting.

Of course, a drawback in any of these light occupations is that by the time one has undressed drowsiness may have fled. That possibility makes it desirable that all preparations for bed shall first be made and a warm robe with comfortable bedroom shoes shall constitute the only extra clothing. Warmth of body, especially of the feet, is essential to sleep. Sometimes so simple a thing as a hot-water bottle at the feet, or even woolen bed-socks, will make all the difference between wakefulness and refreshing slumber.

Then there is the matter of deep breathing, which seems especially adapted to feeble or run-down physiques. That is a large subject more familiar to the people of the Orient than to us. Some Orientals are able to put themselves into trance-like sleep by their knowledge of deep breathing. Numerous books have been written treating of this subject, among the best of which are "The Science of Breath," by Ramacharaka, and "The Law of Rhythmical Breath," by Ella A. Fletcher, though the "Rhythmical Breath" seems fanciful to Western readers.

Sleeplessness is sometimes due to lack of physical exercise, and, when that is so, no device is so effective as work—real physical effort. A great many persons take calisthenic exercises and go in for physical culture to develop muscles and also to regulate circulation so that sleep will come more readily. These are good makeshifts for persons who have no opportunity to work, but, where circumstances make actual labor possible, no substitute can satisfactorily take its place. Gardening, shoveling snow, sawing or chopping wood, all give a variety of motion and a zest of exertion superior to any gymnastics. Even a small amount of some such labor daily will often work a complete cure for insomnia.

Everybody knows of some plan or device for inducing sleep, and all of them are more or less successful—sometimes. Indeed, this is so true that it leads to the belief that, after all, the expectation of sleep helps to bring it, and here suggestion and auto-suggestion come in.

Of late, a number of persons have tried the starvation cure—fasting for several days. This is frequently successful with robust, hearty people, who may unconsciously be eating too much or eating too stimulating food.

Many who feel unequal to a complete fast might cut down the amount of food as much as one-half, with happy results. A vegetarian diet undoubtedly helps, too, although among the lower animals carnivora sleep more than herbivora. The success of vegetarianism, both in insomnia and other diseases, may well be due to the diminished temptation to overeat and the less concentrated diet.

In any event, it is well for the sufferer from sleeplessness to study his own case and experiment with any or all the known devices to see whether, by this means or that, he can lure sleep to his pillow again.

And, speaking of pillows, it is well to remember that one pillow is better than two, and that the one should not be too high, too hard, too soft, or too warm, and that it should be thoroughly aired every day. It should be odorless and cool and have the cover changed frequently. Clean bed linen is in itself an effective device for inducing sleep, just as perfect ventilation adds an hundredfold to the refreshment we get from our slumbers.

The best way to learn to sleep is to practice putting others to sleep. Thy gifts will be unto thyself when thy benefits are to another.

We never know anything thoroughly till we try to teach it. All these plans and devices may be suggested one by one to any sleepless person. Select what you think most suitable and most likely to be accepted, and let the suggestion be that this is a good plan or something just called to your attention that seems sensible. If you do not succeed in one or two, it is difficult to secure trial of more at that time.

Every temperament is different and may respond to different methods: for instance, a ticking clock or dropping water, which make some persons drowsy, will make others inexpressibly nervous.

The trained nurse will tell you that, when you are trying to get the patient to sleep, whispering must not be allowed: the sibilant sound is irritating and the patient unconsciously strains to catch what is said. Speak in a quiet, even, ordinary tone. Do not fuss, putting the shade a little higher and lower, stealing across the room, and so on. If anything is to be done, to walk quietly and naturally will disturb the sleeper much less than tiptoeing about.

That mysterious thing that we call "personality" has much to do with the power to bring sleep to others. Some persons can put almost anyone to sleep by quietly holding the hand, but nearly everyone has some of this power. Some persons, especially children, are readily got to sleep by lying down beside them.

Reading aloud slowly and in a uniform voice will bring sleep to most persons. When drowsiness comes, the voice may be lowered a little and continued until slumber closes the eyes. (Concerning the varieties and causes of Insomnia, see also Appendix A.)

CHAPTER XIX
HYPNOTIC SLEEP

What would we give to our beloved?
The hero's heart to be unmoved,—
   The poet's star-tuned harp to sweep;
The patriot's voice to teach and rouse,—
The monarch's crown to light the brows?
    "He giveth His belovèd sleep."
ELIZABETH BARRETT BROWNING.

THE nature of hypnotic sleep has not yet been fully determined, which is not wonderful when we remember our ignorance of natural sleep. We may call the active hypnotic state a condition of excessive attention to the main idea presented and complete oblivion to other ideas. But this state is preceded by a passive condition resembling sleep. The use and value of hypnotic sleep is now occupying the attention of scientific men and it bids fair to be an important curative agent. Where once the patient suffering from insomnia was treated by drugs, he is now more successfully treated through suggestion. The change is a most desirable one and in line with that newer thought which recognizes the power of regeneration within the soul of the individual. For, the main things in the development of hypnosis and suggestion as curative agents is the recognition that an appeal can be made to the subconscious mind, which, as Dr. Worcester says, "is more sensitive to good and evil than our conscious mind." To appeal to our latent powers to overcome our own weaknesses or limitations is greater and better than to combat these weaknesses through drugs. Many physicians who formerly employed hypnosis have adopted a substitute for it, the so-called hypnoidal state, mere passivity with closed eyes. Hypnotizing is in many cases needless and dangerous.

Insomnia, like any other trouble not due to the breakdown of a physical organ, is more a moral than a material lapse, and can best be cured by moral means: that is, by the aid of the will and its associated faculties. Sleeplessness, nervousness, excitability, and irritability have their rise in mental and emotional states more often than in physical states, and, under such conditions, treatment by drugs is of little real use. In the disease hysteria, mental trouble may masquerade as physical defect, for instance paralysis or even blindness, while the physical parts concerned are in no wise impaired. The dependence placed upon merely extraneous things does not assist in the development of our own inner powers. Even when drugs seem to relieve the outward symptoms, they fail to strengthen the moral nature, so greatly in need of strength. The man of drugs only is at a disadvantage as compared with the suggestionist in treating such disorders. Dr. J. D. Quackenbos says, "The suggestionist invokes the better subliminal self—invests it with control, and seldom fails to effect the desired purpose." He further maintains, what all investigators are now coming to admit, that, when the patient wakes from hypnotic sleep, during which helpful, curative suggestions have been made to him, he is "constrained to obey the impulses of his own superior self." The power of suggestion, whether during waking or sleeping hours, is only beginning to be recognized, although its use in one form or another is centuries old. The thoughtless, as well as the thoughtful, use it more or less every hour of the day, while all of us may know that we are occasionally the victims of auto-suggestion when we suffer from functional ailments.

Auto-suggestion is merely the suggestion of the self to the self, and from ill-advised suggestions spring nearly all the little impediments to sleep and health. Such a suggestion to ourselves as that we need certain favorable conditions for sleeping will keep us awake when those conditions are not possible. We say, "I cannot sleep with a clock ticking in the room with me," and so we lie awake and suffer nervous tortures if we hear a clock tick. Or we say of something our friends do, or of some natural habit they have, "That makes me so nervous I almost fly out of my skin" thus we inflict upon ourselves suffering that we need not endure.

The strong soul will call his "superior self" to his aid to conquer this tendency. He will suggest to himself that he is able to sleep without regard to clocks or other disturbance; that the peculiarities of other people have no power to irritate, annoy, or otherwise upset his nervous system; that even in the midst of alarums he may have peace, if he so wills, and can sleep under ordinary conditions without fear or annoyance.

But, to be able to do this, one must have faith in himself, in his purpose, in his own desire to overcome his fears, for, as Dr. Worcester remarks, "the value of suggestion lies in its character and in the character of the man who makes it." If we say these things to ourselves, feeling all the time that it is useless, we are not likely to impress the subconscious mind or rouse it to activity. Self-deception is not often beneficial in its effects. No more shall we make headway if we merely repeat such suggestions in parrot-fashion. You remember the story of the old woman who heard that faith would remove mountains: so she determined to try it on the hill in front of her bedroom window. All night she repeated to herself that the mountain would be removed. In the morning she awoke to see the hill still in front of her. "There," she said, "I knew it would be." Anyhow, the faith that removes most mountains is the faith that gets a shovel. It is essential that we concentrate our minds upon the matter in hand, excluding from our thoughts anything that might distract us and that we fix our attention upon removing the fault. It is for this reason that the hypnoidal state, or the wakeful night or the moment when one is nearly dropping to sleep is the best time either for suggestion to a patient or for one to indulge in helpful auto-suggestion. As objective consciousness fades, it is easier to impress the subliminal self-consciousness and invoke its aid.

Those who do not know themselves well enough to be able to respond to their own suggestion, may be helped by another in whom they have faith. If they submit themselves willingly to suggestion, they may find themselves so strengthened that they will shortly be able to control themselves by auto-suggestion. Like almost all upward tendencies, this power is a matter of development.

As we come to understand hypnotism better, we learn that we need not fear ill results from thus yielding ourselves for a good purpose to another,[8] for one's subconscious self is always on watch and will not be compelled to do that which is contrary to one's own nature or habit of thought. Hypnotic sleep differs from natural sleep in that the hypnotized person usually preserves a degree of intelligence and invariably a moral sense which are not conspicuous in normal sleep and dreaming. Scientific investigators are quite well agreed on this point, and Dr. Worcester's experience has convinced him of its truth.

So, if all other means of securing sleep should fail, we may have recourse to this newest method of curing nervous and other functional disorders. It is merely one way of getting into closer touch with the Infinite and Universal and coming into line with life's underlying laws.

The use of auto-suggestion is not limited to inducing sleep: it may rid us of evil habits, disturbing thoughts, and all hatred, malice, and uncharitableness—which in their turn interfere with sleep.

THE LAND OF NOD

From breakfast on through all the day
At home among my friends I stay;
But every night I go abroad
Afar into the land of Nod.

All by myself I have to go,
With none to tell me what to do—
All alone beside the streams
And up the mountain-sides of dreams.

The strangest things are there for me,
Both things to eat and things to see,
And many frightening sights abroad
Till morning in the land of Nod.

Try as I like to find the way,
I never can get back by day,
Nor can remember plain and clear
The curious music that I hear.

ROBERT LOUIS STEVENSON.

CHAPTER XX
"PERCHANCE TO DREAM"

"W E are such stuff as dreams are made on," as Shakespeare says, and yet no one even to this day knows what that "stuff" may be. We separate man's life into intellect, feeling, will; or, like the Hindoos, into seven phases; we subdivide these, recognizing special powers and functions belonging to each; we dissect man's frame; we dissolve his body into its component parts, and yet, when all is done, we know as little about *life*, the essence of man, as our father Adam knew. As Omar says, we hear "much talk about it and about" and yet we get nowhere. It is much the same with dreams. We need, therefore, only summarize and review the talk.

Dreams occupied their most important place in the thought of man at its beginning. His action has frequently been directed by a dream and the fate of nations has hinged upon its interpretation. Even in the present day of matter-of-fact science, at some time in his life following the racial bent, almost every human being has paid some attention to his dreams. The superstitious—which includes the most of us—still put faith in their dreams, though they know not whence they come, nor their relation to the most mutable of physical conditions. And this though ages ago Sirach uttered this warning, "Dreams deceive many and fail those who build upon them." Scientific investigation has made known many of the causes of dreams and shown us what slight incidents may determine their direction. For instance, dreams involving hearing often take their rise in noises made by the processes going on in the body. What we eat and the state of our digestion greatly affect the character of our dreams.

This has long been recognized by those who try to decipher special significance in dreams. Twenty-five centuries ago Pythagoras believed that the gas-generating beans destroyed the chance of having enlightening or important dreams, and so forbade their use. In similar fashion interpreters of dreams were warned by Artemidorus to inquire first whether the dreamer had eaten heartily or lightly before falling asleep; while Philostratus maintained that skillful interpreters always refused to expound dreams following the use of wine.

Thus we see that even in ancient times the relation between eating and sleeping was recognized. In more modern days it is recorded that poets and writers had visions from eating raw flesh, while Mrs. Radcliffe, author of "The Mysteries of Udolpho," is said to have deliberately induced horrid dream phantoms by supping late on indigestible food as a means of getting "printer's copy." De Quincey's "Confessions" is a monument to the beauty and the horror of the dreams from drugs. There is also reason to think that the terrors of delirium tremens are true dreams. John B. Gough described from fearful experience the agony of seeing and feeling that which is dreadful, mainly because the sufferer knows that it, nevertheless, does not exist and could not exist. This can be explained, in our present state of knowledge, only by the supposition that the subconscious mind, uncorrected and unrestrained by the senses, alone is awake. Boris Sidis shows that we have no waking remembrance of many of our dreams, even of most harassing ones.

It is probable that perfect sleep is undisturbed by dreams, pleasant or otherwise. Dreams are an evidence of the semi-conscious condition of some of the senses; the objective mind is no longer in control, but is passive, and the subjective mind is active. Yet while dreaming, the objective mind is not so completely unconscious (as it would be if wrapped in profound slumber) but that it gets glimpses of the workings of the subjective mind, often very distorted glimpses. This frequently leads to horrible or impossible situations in dreams.

It is an interesting question how far we are responsible for our dreams. It is true in dreams, as in waking, that from the same sensations individuals will evolve different results, just as nasturtiums, drawing nourishment from the same soil, will put forth blossoms of different color and odor. The factor that changes these same elements into different results is something inherent in the individual person or plant.

So that we are not entirely responsible for what we dream, yet the mental habits, the real tone of mind maintained during waking hours, has its effect upon dreams. They constitute an index of the mind. So far as sleep is concerned, of course, "subjective" mind is simply our remembered experiences, our mental capital, and can be used in waking hours and is constantly so used: we get traces of these in our dreams. Age, sex, and temperament also affect the nature of dreams.

If then our sleep is disturbed by unpleasant dreams, it becomes necessary to investigate the causes. Have we eaten too much or too hurriedly? Are our innermost thoughts clean and wholesome, fit for the light of day? Roman philosophers held that he who wished to obtain knowledge of the will of any of the gods, must fast and lie down to sleep beside the shrine of the god, his thoughts filled with longing and desire for such knowledge. There is more than mere superstition in that. If we abstain from all excesses and are filled with desire to know the will of the gods, dreams, when they come to us, will not disturb or distress us.

Dreams are admittedly sometimes prophetic, or have at least an indirect significance touching events not yet come to pass. Galen tells of a man who dreamed that his leg had turned to stone, and a few days later found his leg paralyzed, perhaps an instance of auto-suggestion. Gessner died from a malignant growth which developed in his breast in the exact spot where, a few nights previously, he had dreamed that a serpent bit him; while Aristides, dreaming that he was wounded in the knee by a bull, awoke to find a tumor there.

These and many better authenticated cases of dream warnings are not so strange as they seem at first hearing. They may be explained largely by the fact that remote and vague sensations of suffering and disease are able to make deeper impression upon the mind when the interests and activities of the waking life are submerged in sleep.

The duration of dreams is another matter of great interest. Most persons feel and say that they "dreamed all night long," and will proceed to support their statement by relating various incidents of their dreams; their prolonged sensations of pleasure or horror; the events that perhaps covered years. Yet, in reality, the dream may have occupied less than a minute. The dreamer cannot measure the time spent in dreaming, for the unconscious condition of the objective mind obliterates the sense of time, space or material limitations. This accounts for the prodigious feats, the marvels and impossible achievements of dreams that seem to the dreamer in no way disproportionate.

What we do know is that some of the most wonderful dreams have occupied but a few moments, and so far scientific research seems to limit them to an hour or two at most. Mohammed's dream was completed within the time occupied by a falling vase; and it is on record that a man fell asleep just as the clock struck the first stroke of twelve and awoke in a cold sweat on the last stroke, having dreamed that he had spent thirty years in prison, suffering tortures of mind and body.

All this makes it easy to understand how, to an infinite mind, a thousand years may be as one day and one day as a thousand years, and how, in our degree, the quiet, self-controlled mind may be unmoved by time.

It is the vivid impression made by such dreams that makes us feel that they must have lasted a long time. Then, as George Trumbull Ladd says, the recital of our dreams is often colored, unconsciously, "by our self-conscious and rational waking life when we bring the scene before the awakened mind." In other words, many sensations that we think we experienced are heightened by the idea in the objective mind of what such sensations ought to be.

It may be that when the time comes that

"No one shall work for money
And no one shall work for fame,"

we shall find light and help in our dreams that is undreamed of now.

CHAPTER XXI
NATURAL LIVING

Sleep, the saint that evil thoughts and aims
Takest away, and into souls dost creep,
Like to a breeze from heaven.
                                        WORDSWORTH.

HE who would get the benefit of sleep must look after health.

Health, after all, is merely that condition where all parts of the human organism work together without friction. We think of health as something that is bestowed upon us from without; something over which we have no control and almost no influence. Perhaps this queer idea is partly responsible for the general lack of health to-day.

It seems incredible that it is necessary that human beings endowed with tremendous capacity for enjoyment, with everything at hand to enjoy, should be hindered by a mere lack of that harmony that we call health from fully enjoying life. It seems only reasonable that there must be some explanation of lack of health and some way of escape from it.

It is now generally admitted that most of the diseases to which man thinks himself heir are due to improper, unnatural living. It could safely be added that the remainder of our ill-health and distress comes in large part from improper, unnatural thinking.

The common man may laugh at the idea that we make our own ill-health; if you were not more intelligent than the common man, you would not read this book, so that you will probably see at once that your own experience has taught you the truth of it. You will discover that you have learned for yourself, albeit for the most part unconsciously, that what a man thinks about, that he becomes. So it would seem that the natural and proper thing to do, if we find ourselves suffering from sleeplessness and ill-health, is to look after our way of living and thinking.

Medical science was once the attempt to cure disease; as Dr. Woods Hutchinson says, it is now coming to be the science of preventing disease, and everything that tends to that end is properly a part of the science of medicine, though it have no connection with the myriad drugs of the pharmacopœia.

Until we compare conditions to-day with those of even fifty years ago, we can form no idea of our rapid strides toward natural living. If we walk the streets of the city or the roads of suburban towns and villages very early in the morning, at any season of the year, we shall find the vast majority of the houses with open windows. It is true that the opening may not always be very wide, but they are open. Fifty years ago all would have been closed.

Within the recollection of those whose memories go back a quarter of a century, we were taught that night air was dangerous to breathe and was to be completely shut out from our houses. Now we know that the organism needs fresh air by night as well as by day, and that the most dangerous thing about night air is the lack of it.

We now treat the most dreaded diseases, pneumonia and tuberculosis, almost wholly by fresh air and nourishing food, administering drugs only to check the symptoms until the system gets into condition to throw them off. More than that, we know now that consumption, at least, is not a mysterious dispensation of Providence visited upon certain people without regard to individual responsibility. Rather it is always the result of improper living or thinking, or both, and, when it is the scourge of a district, as in thickly settled city slums, it is the direct result of monopoly and oppression that deny the common interests of all mankind.

In 1865 Dr. W. W. Hall of New York published his book, "Sleep," in the preface of which he said: "It is the end and aim of this book to show that as a means of high health, good blood, and a strong mind to old and young, sick or well, each one should have a single bed in a large, clean, light room, so as to pass all the hours of sleep in a pure, fresh air, and that those who fail in this, will in the end fail in health and strength of limb and brain, and will die while yet their days are not all told." That this physician with a large practice should find it necessary to write a book to set forth the necessity of fresh air during sleeping-hours, goes to show how little the mass of our people knew even fifty years ago. We hear so much about fresh air in these days that we forget that the preceding generation was in deadly terror of it.

All things point to a marked advance during the past decades, in the understanding of conditions necessary for health, but, after all, we have come but a very little way along the road we must travel to get the most out of life.

We owe a good deal of our advance in this direction to physicians and others who have broken loose from traditions and have not feared to put their ideas and discoveries to the test. Nature has provided all things for "the healing of the nations," if we but trust her. As Dr. Shattuck, a famous Boston surgeon, used to say in making his rounds in the Massachusetts General Hospital, "There is one inestimable gift God has given to man—an abundance of fresh air." It was his method of announcing that he did not think the ventilation of room or ward was sufficient, and the nurses understood that, and immediately admitted more air into the room.

In the wards of that great institution were dozens of persons who had never before heard of the value of fresh air: being compelled by evil social conditions to live in districts where sunshine and air were rarities, they had never heard of any relation between health and fresh air. They frequently learned that lesson there.

A little device which we call "the Perfect Gift of Sleep" is a great help in excluding the light without excluding the air, and especially valuable in that most delightful change, sleeping out of doors. A bag is made of dark green or blue or black silk or satin, about four inches wide and eight inches long, and very loosely filled with sweet pine needles. It is laid lightly over the eyes.

This may seem too trivial to bother about, but the increased comfort and the better quality of sleep which it brings is astonishing.

CHAPTER XXII
FRESH AIR AND REFRESHING SLEEP

Somnus, that walks the world from twilights' wane
All the night long till day be born again.
EDGAR FAWCETT.

I T is not so necessary now as when Dr. Hall wrote to urge the importance of large, airy sleeping-rooms. But it is amazing to find how many, even among the so-called "better classes," neglect to open their windows wide at night. I have known people out in the country whose bedroom windows could hardly be made to open, so seldom did they admit the air. Indeed, they were also heavily shaded so that they might not admit the sunshine.

That such people have been able to live at all is due to the patience of Nature, or to the fact that so much of the day is spent in the open air that it helps to counteract the effect of the closed-up night. Even then they do not escape early wrinkles, bent shoulders, and a look of age long before their time. We used to attribute these to the hard work of the farmer's life, but we might more properly attribute it to improper living.

Besides an abundance of fresh air day and night, summer and winter, personal cleanliness immensely aids to health and the ability to sleep. In the old days we bathed to clean ourselves when dirty. It was an advance on that when someone said he took a bath every spring and fall, whether he needed it or not. In those days once a week was considered frequent. To-day we bathe to keep clean.

Someone, probably Joseph Fels, has said that the civilization of a people may best be estimated by the amount of soap and water it consumes. If we start out well-groomed in the morning—fresh from the bath with clean linen, clothes brushed and all our personal needs duly attended to—we carry our heads higher, feel an uplift of body and mind that is impossible to the careless or untidy person.

The same influence applies to going to bed at night. If we retire soiled and worn from the day's experiences, we may toss and turn with discomfort whose source we may not understand, or we fall into heavy, unrefreshing sleep. The body does most of its breathing during sleeping-time. You know how the moisture from the breath shows on a mirror when you breathe on it: well, the skin gives off about three times as much moisture as the breath, and, unless the pores of the skin are free from all obstructions such as dust, old, dried perspiration, and similar soil, it cannot perform its work properly and to the advantage of the sleeper. If you don't like water, use oil as the Easterns do. Even dry rubbing, if the skin is moist, will keep the pores open.

The little trouble entailed is more than offset by the refreshed feeling, the lightening of the mind as well as of the body, the more restful sleep, and the better health resulting from the practice.

One of the advantages of the night bath is that it reminds us to change all the clothes we have worn during the day. If they must be worn again the next day, they should be spread out on the backs of chairs or on hangers, that they may be thoroughly aired before morning. If we feel that we must have something more than the pajamas or night-robe, then there should be separate sets of underclothes kept for that purpose alone—old, thin, partly-worn ones may be reserved for this use.

Whether baths should be hot, warm, or cold must depend upon the individual. There is no set rule that applies equally to all persons. Many persons find the cold plunge or shower most invigorating in the morning,—it is too stimulating to be taken at night—and others cannot stand the shock of contact with cold water at any time. There is but one wise thing to do—to experiment for yourself and adopt the sort of bath that seems best suited to your needs. Most people will find the warm bath more satisfactory than the hot or cold.

And remember that it is not only the lungs that need fresh air: the skin needs it too, and, next to overeating, the quickest way to "catch" cold is to bundle up in heavy perspiration-holding flannels. Linen mesh is excellent, but, whatever underclothing is worn, it should not suffocate the millions of pores of the skin.

An airy room, free from hangings, carpets, street clothes, and all other dust-gatherers; a clean body; a contented mind—these are important factors both in sleep and in general health, and, best of all, they are inexpensive enough to be within the reach of nearly everybody.

CHAPTER XXIII
THE BREATH OF LIFE

In winter I get up at night
And dress by yellow candle-light.
In summer, quite the other way,
I have to go to bed by day.

I have to go to bed and see
The birds still hopping on the tree,
Or hear the grown-up people's feet
Still going past me in the street.

And does it not seem hard to you,
When all the sky is clear and blue,
And I should like so much to play,
To have to go to bed by day?
    "Bed in Summer."

Robert Louis Stevenson.

O NE of the most common causes of ill-health and sleeplessness is improper breathing. Breathing is the fundamental function of life, the first at birth and the last at death, and when it is badly performed we are sure to have trouble. The great majority of people never use the whole of their lungs in breathing. By this neglect the blood is never sufficiently oxygenated to burn out all impurities.

But you may say, "I am not responsible for the way I breathe; I do that "automatically," and you would be in a degree correct. It is true that we are not conscious of the act of breathing. It would be an intolerable burden upon the mind if every breath required conscious attention. We could hardly attend to anything else.

That is no reason, however, why we should not regulate our breathing for our own benefit. Breathing, though an habitual organic act, is under the indirect control of the higher centers of the nervous system. We must, as Dr. Worcester says, re-educate the lower centers to breathe, and to do this it is necessary to give conscious attention to it for a time. If we wish to replace bad breathing by good breathing, we must fix our attention regularly upon drawing the breath, practice the right sort of breathing, and impress upon the vital mechanism that this new order of breathing is to be adopted, for the way to be rid of a bad habit is to replace it with a good one. If we persevere in this course, the right method can very easily be established.

By the right method is meant breathing from the diaphragm. If you will watch the act of breathing among your friends for even one day, you will discover for yourself how few do it well. The great majority breathe with the upper part of the lungs only, so that the chest visibly rises and falls in time with the inhalations and exhalations. Such persons may be unconscious of their own breathing, but they make all who observe them conscious of it. They are not only injuring themselves, but making a claim upon the attention of others that is scarcely justifiable.

Quick, short breathing is one of the signs either of excitement or of depression, some pleasurable or painful emotion or sensation, but it is not a means to health. If we have this habit, we may find in it an explanation of many of the trifling ills and discomforts from which we suffer, and of not a few of the more serious ones.

Emily M. Bishop, who has given much study to the effect of our habits of mind and body upon our health and spirits, says, in her latest book, "Daily Ways of Living," that we may change the whole current of our thought by a change in breathing. She wisely advises her readers the next time they feel depressed or worried, "blue," or "miserable," to try drawing deep, full breaths. If you are not in good spirits, try that now: "spirit" means the breath.

Open the windows and let in fresh air, if within doors; inhale deeply, hold it, and then exhale rather quickly. After only four or five such inhalations you will find that the miserable feeling has disappeared or is greatly lessened. The "blues" cannot live while good red blood is circulating rapidly through the veins and arteries. It is only when the blood is sluggish or not sufficiently purified by the indrawn oxygen that worry and depression can hold us in their thrall. Deep breathing is a simple remedy for the blues, but its effectiveness makes it worth trying.

Proper breathing will often ward off a cold, especially a cold due to chill. As soon as you feel yourself getting chilly, act. The feeling of chilliness is a proof that the resistance of the body is below normal. The cause may be interior, due to the presence of some poison in the system, or it may be due entirely to external causes. In either event, to purify the blood and improve its circulation is the best sort of "first aid to the injured." Inhale until you can feel it in your fingers and toes, exhale quickly, and repeat the operation until you feel all aglow. Mlle. Marie de Palkowska, whose special work is teaching correct breathing, says: "The nerve centers are directly affected by the condition of the blood, and they are enfeebled, contracted, or irritated by an excess of carbon and nitrogen in it, producing depression of spirits; but, if the blood is circulating freely, the nerves are quieted and well-nourished by the supply of oxygen, through the process of correct breathing, and the result is perfect health of mind and body and a happy optimism." Worry, sleeplessness, and disease do not easily lay hold upon one who has "perfect health of mind and body and a happy optimism." If these may be secured through intelligent attention to breathing, there is no reason why they should not be as common as they are natural. The more we look into the question of health, whether physical, mental, or moral, the more clearly we see that poise is only possible through conformity to universal law. It could not be otherwise.

Earlier in this inquiry we have traced the interdependence, the unity of man's three natures—the physical, the mental, and the spiritual,—and the value of correct breathing to the whole man is in perfect keeping with that interdependence. In the process of digestion, upon which physical health so largely depends, we create poisons within ourselves and accumulate waste matter. The organism must be momently purified of these wastes, or putrefaction quickly follows. Autotoxins form, as the doctors say. The function of breathing, when properly controlled, affords the quickest and best method of cleansing the blood of these impurities. If we have not this proper control, the poisons are not eliminated and the supply of blood to the brain is vitiated.

Just as the body cannot perform its functions well if we are compelled to live upon tainted food, so the brain cannot do its work well if the blood—its food—is impure. Breathing which expands the diaphragm so purifies the blood as it passes through the lungs, that it becomes an important factor in maintaining health and poise in body and mind, which in their turn react upon the spirit.

This sort of breathing is more common among men than among women, due in part to natural physical differences and in part to dress. Man breathes largely from the abdomen, while woman breathes chiefly from the chest, expanding only the upper portion of the lungs. This is partly a natural and partly an artificial necessity, due to the pressure of the corset upon the diaphragm. Both men and women would find their physical health improved and their outlook on life broadened and brightened by proper control of the function of breathing. If we are sleepless, nervous, too alert, as well as if we are heavy, dull, and inactive, we will find it worth our while to try conscious breath control. It takes but a comparatively short time to re-educate the automatic centers into correct breathing and the result is always good.

It no less behooves the man who is trying to live largely on the rational plane, than the man who is living wholly on the physical plane, to make his efforts both easier and more effective by such simple attention to natural laws. The next time you are worried, depressed, or sleepless, change the air of the room and try deep and correct breathing for a few minutes. You will be surprised at the complete change wrought in you, if you are not suffering from some serious organic breakdown which needs skilled attention. And even that condition may be helped by proper breathing.

But we are not to forget that, like calisthenic and gymnastic exercises, the training of the breathing is really little more than a device for correcting the results of wrong living and only a substitute for right living. The man or the woman who does plenty of healthful, normal work, who often pants and gets "out of breath," naturally expands the lungs and has as little use for breathing exercises as for tight clothing.

A buck-saw, a spade, or even a broom is better than a teacher of breathing and a better corrector of sleeplessness.

CHAPTER XXIV.
EATING AND SLEEPING

For his sleep
Was aery light, from pure digestion bred.
MILTON.

W E do not have to depend upon mere irresponsible guesses for the new faith in the possibility of longer life for man. Scientists have been experimenting along this line for some years, and Metchnikoff assures us that the average human life should exceed "three-score years and ten" by four decades.

He points out that the greatly increased number of persons who remain physically and mentally active past the age of seventy-five and eighty years is itself a proof that life may be prolonged. He recognizes that merely to extend existence is not a sufficient end to work for—it must be an active, worthwhile existence, and he has experimented toward this end.

All of us can recall instances of "old people" who have preserved their physical and mental faculties until their last years. We have been in the habit of regarding these people as exceptions and have perhaps not noticed that these "exceptions" are already almost frequent enough to prove that there is no such rule for longevity.

Whenever we investigate a new and wonderful thing, we find that its causes are simple and ordinary. So Metchnikoff and kindred experimenters are beginning to show us that prolonging life is a comparatively simple matter. It comes back again to diet and sleep on the physical side and to understanding of the universal laws on the mental and the emotional side of life.

All scientific men agree that nearly all of us eat too much, or eat improper food. Most of them say that we sleep too much, or try to sleep too much. They advise simple diet, varied but not heavy. It is probable that the early human being ate as the wild animals do, to appease hunger, and had to eat whatever he could find without regard to taste. As civilization advanced and he learned ways of getting increased returns from Nature, he began to select and choose what he should eat. In this way he developed "appetite" as apart from natural hunger, and as his knowledge increased, and his taste became more and more refined, appetite gradually took the place of hunger.

People ordinarily seldom know the pleasure of satisfying real hunger. Because of habit, the appetite stirs as often as three or five times a day and we gratify it. We must have certain foods prepared in a certain way. Eating becomes an end in itself, rather than merely a means to an end. If appetite is fully indulged, he becomes heavy, suffers from indigestion and sleeplessness, talks of stomach trouble and consequent "loss of appetite." He seeks a physician to restore what he is really better without. Not every physician is as wise as the one to whom a cook once applied. She told her story of inability to eat her meals, of uncertain and unrestful sleep, increased weight, and shortness of breath. The physician heard her tale of woe and asked her the size of the family for which she cooked and about their mode of living. He learned that the family consisted of five, and that they entertained lavishly. "Do you taste all the food you prepare?" was the next question.

"Yes, sir; I must taste it to be sure it is just right." "Ah!" replied the doctor; "put on a plate exactly the same quantity of everything that you take to taste—no more, no less—and send it to me to-morrow evening."

Much to the cook's astonishment, at the close of the next day, which had included a dinner-party, there was a heaping platter of food, more than she would have thought it possible to eat even at three meals.

"It is not a tonic you want," said the physician. "You already eat too much, which accounts for your loss of appetite, shortness of breath, and sleeplessness. It may be necessary for you to taste all the food you cook, but take smaller 'tastes' and eat nothing else on cooking days. I cannot help you; you must help yourself." (Being an ignorant woman, she went to another doctor and got some ill-tasting drug.)

And such is, after all, the decision of all the scientific investigators into the life and health of men: We must help ourselves by understanding the laws of life and observing them.

Most rich persons are really like the man who applied to his physician about "loss of appetite." "Try beginning dinner with raw oysters," said the doctor. In a few days the patient returned, to say that the oysters did no good.

"Maybe you didn't eat enough?" said the doctor.

"Well," said the man, "I ate four dozen."

CHAPTER XXV
SLEEPING AND EATING

Man's rich restorative, his balmy bath
That supplies, lubricates and keeps in play
The various movements of this nice machine.
                                    YOUNG.

"THERE are more things in heaven and earth than are dreamt of" in anybody's philosophy or understanding of living; it is not strange that the great mass have not dreamed of eating as a cause of sleeplessness and ill-health, though they may dream in consequence of it. It is generally believed that a hearty meal of any indigestible food immediately before bed is bad for sleep: yet animals and primitive men always sleep after they are gorged. But few recognize that the whole plan of eating may be responsible for sleeplessness or excessive sleepiness. For, like fatigue, food may either bring or prevent sleep.

In these days not even the most fastidious will object to a discussion of the ethics and æsthetics of feeding. It is no longer "the gratification of a vulgar necessity," but a matter of keen scientific interest. Colleges give courses in the chemistry of food that we may know what combinations it is wise to make, while some of the leading universities have made severe practical tests of some of the new "fads in eating." There are so many theories of eating to-day that one may take his choice, and, if the quality of both health and sleep is not improved, he can run through the list and then take what is best of each.

When Dr. W. W. Hall wrote his book on fresh air in the sleeping-room, he added, in a casual sort of way, this piece of advice to the would-be sleeper, "Always eat slowly and in moderation of well-divided food." That is advice that will bear infinite repetition. It is really the keynote of all the present-day theories of eating. It applies equally well to omnivorous and vegetarian peoples.

Horace Fletcher says, "You may eat anything you like, if you eat it at the right time and in the right way," and, when one has learned what Mr.

Fletcher thinks is the right time and way, one has grasped the whole of "Fletcherism." It consists in eating only when one is hungry—so hungry that "the mouth waters and one could stand and whinny like a horse at the smell of bread"—and then chewing just as long as there is any taste left to the food. I have known children to get the habit of eating too fast, with indigestion and restlessness as a consequence, because the nurse stood beside the table with a spoonful always ready and waiting while the last was being swallowed. We may avoid that habit for ourselves or cure ourselves of it by always laying down the knife and fork or spoon after each mouthful. This insures some time to chew.

It is the opinion of all those who have special theories on "what to eat and how to eat it" that civilized man scarcely knows what true hunger is. We are so in the habit of eating at fixed and customary hours that we create "habit hunger," which has but slight connection with Nature's demands for sustenance. In accordance with this idea, fasting is again becoming popular and all sorts of good results are claimed for it. The "devil of unrest and disease" is now being reckoned among "those that go not out but by fasting and prayer." Fasting and prayer meant the physical and the spiritual treatment together.

Fasting has long been imposed upon man as a religious rite, generally as penance for some "sin," but now it is being advised and self-imposed for the sake of its physical advantages. It may well be that the habit of fasting for health's sake originated with prehistoric man and was diverted into religious channels and its original significance forgotten. So many "religious rites" have come about in this way that it is fair to assume that fasting may have, also.

However that may be, the practice is coming into scientific prominence, and Charles C. Haskell in his book, "Perfect Health: How to Get it and How to Keep it, by One Who Has It," made much of the importance of fasting. If one is ill, fasting will make him well, according to Mr. Haskell. He gives numerous instances of the benefits that have followed fasts extending from one to nine or even more days. Mr. Upton Sinclair has written of his happy experience of abstinence in "The Fasting Cure." As soon as the system is ready for food, true hunger will appear, says Mr. Haskell, and, like Mr. Fletcher, he regards "watering at the mouth"—the free flow of saliva—as the best index of real hunger.

But, unlike Fletcher, Haskell is a vegetarian pure and simple, as that word is generally understood. Haskell says, "Nature has provided a natural food for man, and it is the vegetable kingdom." He also strongly urges upon the seeker for sound health, which means sound sleep, to give up the habit of taking breakfast, thus conquering appetite and restoring real hunger. This is, indeed, the first precept he lays down; and the second is much like it. It runs, "Never eat except at the call of Natural Hunger." Third, "Enjoy to the full every mouthful of food as long as any taste remains in it." Fourth, "Do not drink any liquids with your meals." The rules are simple enough to follow if you have any cause to suspect that your mode of life is the cause of "poor sleep." This book has no special brand of food to recommend, nor does it intend to say what any man should or should not eat. Sir Henry Thompson is about right when he says that "No man can tell another what he can or ought to eat, without knowing what are the habits of life and work —mental and bodily—of the person to be advised. One rule cannot apply to all."

All that the writer aims to do is to set forth the best theories of how to insure sound sleep and good health, and to leave it to the individual reader to try whichever he thinks fits. It is what he will do, anyway, if he is a wise man; for only by following the course he most desires can he learn whether these desires are to be trusted as guides to happiness and well-being.

But—most persons eat too much or too often or too fast. Maybe you do, too.

CHAPTER XXVI
SOME MODERN THEORIES OF SLEEP

I have an exposition of sleep come upon me.
SHAKESPEARE.

THERE have been almost as many theories of sleep and its causes as there have been investigators, but these theories may be grouped under a few main heads:

Physiological, or that which has to do with some bodily conditions only, and which made men think that sleep was dependent upon the circulation of the blood or upon decreased consumption of oxygen, was an early one of these theories. It has had many advocates and has led to many interesting experiments that have increased the sum of general knowledge, although they have not explained sleep.

Delicate instruments, with formidable names, have been invented and successfully used to measure the intensity of sleep and to note its phenomena. Two of the experimenters—C. E. Brush, Jr., and R. Fayerweather of the Physiological Laboratory of Johns Hopkins University —through long, intricate and exhaustive experiments, have found that sleep is most intense and the pressure of blood in the arteries lowest during the first half of the sleeping period. After we have completed the first half of our sleep, the intensity or soundness of sleep becomes less, and the pressure of blood in the arteries continues to increase up to the moment of awaking.

It is interesting to learn that the moment when we are most soundly sleeping is at the end of the first hour of sleep, and that the blood-pressure has at that time reached its very lowest point. Messrs. Brush and Fayerweather report that, during the first few hours of sleep, the blood-pressure continues to fall and then begins a gradual rise. The tendency is to more and more rapid flow of the blood, but this rise is not steady or regular, because it is broken by long waves when the force of the circulation falls and the pulse is weaker than it was a moment or two before. The rapidity of the blood-flow is greater on the moment of awakening than just before dropping to sleep. This increase is not sudden, but is the culmination of the rise that begins a few hours after we fall asleep. (See Appendix B.)

The intensity or depth of sleep is shown by a curve that looks like a pile of sand with the top scooped off. It increases rather slowly, in most cases, for the first quarter-hour: then quickly, so that half an hour later the person is most "sound asleep." He stays so, on the level top, for about half an hour. That is the time that wise burglars and late husbands choose to steal into the house, about an hour after everyone is asleep. After that time the sleeper reverses the process of falling into deep sleep by getting nearer to waking for half an hour and then getting, at first rapidly, nearer to waking for two or three hours. In the last three or four hours healthy and normal persons reach about the same proportions of time and intensity of sleep, so that the Indian-bow-shaped curve fairly represents how long it takes everybody to deepen his sleep. Kohlschütter found how great an intensity of sound was needed to awaken a sleeper at different periods throughout the night. His curve thus made tallies very exactly with that of Brush and Fayerweather, obtained in quite a different way.

Some other investigators have pointed out that, interesting as this theory is, it proves one thing about as completely as it does the other. For, while it is plain that sleep and the great fall in blood-pressure exist at the same moment, it is not conclusively shown which is cause and which is effect. Does sleep cause the fall in blood-pressure, or does the fall in blood-pressure cause sleep? The two are coexistent, but who can say which begins first?

It looks as if sleep might be more justly considered the cause, if one takes the sleeping-position, and maintains the attitude of mind suitable to induce sleep, blood-pressure grows less, even though the patient does not actually fall asleep.

Under this physiological view must come also the chemical theory based on the fact that we consume more oxygen during the day, thus forming carbon dioxide and other poisons which cause sleepiness. During the night we absorb oxygen, building up the tissues, and eliminating the poisons of the waking hours.

The poisons which are the result of the consumption of oxygen cause fatigue, and according to Preyer, a European authority, "sleep is the direct consequence of fatigue, or rather of the fatigue products in the blood." His contention is that, if lactic acid and other chemical products of the consumption of oxygen in the body were injected artificially, sleep would follow. Experiments in this direction made by Preyer, Fisher, and L. Meyer have yielded such contradictory results that the theory is not proved thereby.

The idea that sleep is the result of poisons in the system takes us into the pathological theory of sleep, which regards it as a sort of disease like epilepsy or auto-intoxication. We produce by our own activities the poisons which cause insensibility until the system cleanses itself. Professor Leo Errera of Brussels says that "work in the organism is closely bound up with a chemical breaking down." Among the products of this breakdown are "leucomaines," the scientific name for poisons formed in living tissue, and just the opposite to "ptomaines," which, however, are also virulent poisons.

Professor Errera tells us that, during our waking hours, we produce more leucomaines than the oxygen we absorb can destroy. This excess is carried along by the blood and held by the brain centers, and in time produces sleep, just as any poisonous anæsthetic, such as morphine, would produce sleep.

While we are sleeping we absorb much oxygen and we recover from the effects of our self-intoxication. Errera maintains that work, fatigue, sleep, and repair are not merely successive events, but phenomena chained together in a regular and necessary cycle. He explains sleeplessness due to overfatigue on the theory that small doses of poisons induce sleep and large doses induce excitement and even convulsions.

Manacéïne points out that this theory is good from a purely physical standpoint, but does not explain our power to postpone sleep or the faculty of waking at a fixed hour. We can do both, and any adequate theory of sleep must explain why we can control the tendency to sleep, but cannot control the symptoms of ordinary poisoning.

CHAPTER XXVII
EARLY THEORIES OF SLEEP

Balm that tames all anguish.
WORDSWORTH.

M R. EDWARD BINNS of London, as early as 1842, published a book called "The Anatomy of Sleep"—with the subtitle, "The Art of Procuring Sound and Refreshing Slumber at Will." The subtitle makes one think of the three-volume novels of that time, but the book is fairly concise and worth careful review. Moreover, it is in advance of many works on sleep both before and after. (For ancient surmises see Appendix C.)

One of the favorite medical theories of sleep is that it is caused by fatigue, and is, therefore, purely passive in its nature. Binns did not accept this theory. He said, "Sleep is an active and positive faculty, not a negative and passive result of fatigue or weariness." Some of the more modern writers, notably Manacéïne, agree with Dr. Binns that sleep is not the result of physical fatigue or weariness. Dr. Binns thinks that one proof that fatigue can in no sense be said to be the cause of sleep is that, if we prolong "the state of wakefulness after the usual period of retiring to rest, it is more difficult to induce sleep than if we went at the usual hour." This is especially true of children, yet the patient may be much more fatigued at the later hour than at the usual bedtime.

Binns' theory is that physiological sleep is in antagonism to intellectual activity, being the active process of nutrition, assimilation of food, or of the repair of the waste of the body; that it concerns the nerve centers: that is, "the ganglionic system." It is a generally admitted theory that man's activity, whether physical or mental, "uses up" tissue and nerve force, and that it is only when repair exceeds this waste that life is maintained at a high standard. If the activities of life be many and varied, much sleep according to this theory would be needed to repair the waste of force. Experience has shown that those who live purely physical lives, doing hard manual labor with little mental exercise, need the most sleep. Those whose activities are mostly mental generally sleep fewer hours, though the desire for sleep may be as intense when it comes as is that of the manual laborer. (See Appendix, Questionnaire.)

Regarding sleep as a necessity, in itself an "active and positive faculty," Binns says of it that "it is the true 'vis medicatrix naturæ' —the healing force of nature—to whose vigilance we are indebted for that condition of mind and body called 'health.'" However, he is not an advocate of long hours of sleep for everybody. He thinks individuals differ widely in the amount of sleep needed. He makes the general statement that, "the lower the cerebral organs in the scale of organization, the greater the power of sleep." On this point all the authorities agree, and even in our own experience we learn that. The animals nearest to man in point of development sleep more than man sleeps; and, among men, those who live the most sluggish mental and emotional lives sleep longer than those whose brains are more active.

There may, of course, be exceptions to this rule, and yet those exceptions would not disprove that there is a rule. Much depends, says the good doctor, upon the peculiarities "of the individual; the culture of his mind; his amusement, his food, his occupation, and the temper with which he wooes sleep. General Elliot never slept more than four hours out of twenty-four, and his food consisted wholly of bread, vegetables, and water." This seems like one more link in the chain that binds up our habits of eating with our power to sleep. Just as heavy eating late at night may so disturb our slumber as to leave us practically sleepless, so general heavy eating may render us so incapable of mental activity that sleep may take possession of us. General Elliot's slight need of sleep was probably due, in large measure, to his light diet, and Dr. Binns seems to be of that opinion. We notice that flesh-eating animals, especially serpents, gorge and then sleep long.

A modern medical authority, Sir Henry Thompson of London, in his book, "Diet in Relation to Age and Activity," takes somewhat similar ground, although careful to state that he is not "a vegetarian." He says: "I have been compelled by facts to accept the conclusion that as much mischief in the form of actual disease, impaired vigor and shortened life accrues to civilized man, so far as I have observed in our own country and throughout almost every part of Europe, from erroneous habits in eating as from the habitual use of alcoholic drink, considerable as I know the evil of that to be."[9]

CHAPTER XXVIII
MORE THEORIES

To Sleep I give my powers away
My will is bondsman to the dark;
I sit within a helmless bark.

TENNYSON.

THERE is another class of investigators who aim to explain what might be called the nervous mechanism of sleep rather than its causes. These are the histologists, and theirs is the "histological" theory of sleep. There is a vast literature on this one phase of sleep theorizing alone, and it is deeply interesting to those who, in order to understand this theory, are willing to wrestle with the difficult and technical terms.

The general reader, unfamiliar with physiological terms, is bewildered by such a word as "neuroglia." He wonders what sort of a fossil that is, when in fact it is merely a particular sort of tissue found in the central nervous system; a substance without any nervous property serving a purpose merely similar to cement. So that, after all, like much science, it is simple enough when put in plain words.

Some histologists hold that the neuroglia is able to contract or expand; that, when expanded, it takes or receives impressions from without, and, when it contracts, it shuts out such impressions, thus inducing sleep. Dr. J. Leonard Corning, of New York, says that "Sleep may be defined as that state of the central nervous system in which the higher centers are, to a great extent, in a condition of physiological quiescence, with all the consequences thereby implied." Dr. Corning means that the nervous centers of the brain are inactive, as a result of contraction, and that this state results in drowsiness and in consequent loss of the consciousness. He recognizes, however, that this purely physical condition does not always produce sleep; that there may be disturbing causes within. He says: "Those who suffer from sleeplessness are, almost without exception, beset by a variety of disagreeable mental symptoms during the day, dread of impending evil, irritability, depression, dread of society, etc." Although these are often the result of wrong states of mind or heart, he recommends for such cases warm baths, Turkish baths, massage, and for obstinate cases he even suggests the use of drugs, because he regards the formation of habits of insomnia as more likely than the formation of the drug habit. This suggestion is not generally favored by the investigators of sleep, the most of whom discountenance the use of drugs. Almost everyone has known somebody who contracted the "drug habit," or has heard of somebody who died from the effects of an overdose of some poison taken to induce sleep. Nobody should dose himself with drugs, hoping to get good results from sleep thus secured. It is wiser by far to discover the cause of sleeplessness and remove it, rather than merely to stupefy ourselves for the time being.

It was as a worker along histological lines that Henry Hubbard Foster of Cornell University became convinced that sleep is induced by the absence of stimuli: that is, of things that attract and hold our attention. It may be that the individual withdraws from all stimulating conditions and creates conditions to cause sleep, as we do when we prepare for bed; or it may be that, because of fatigue, our senses do not respond to the things that would otherwise stimulate us. In either event, the result is the same—there is an absence of stimuli.

Foster believes that the present state of our development is not sufficient to meet the demands of continuous activity of the senses and the brain. "If it were not for fatigue," he says, "the development of the nervous system might be carried to such a point that consciousness could be present continuously." He finds the reason for sleep in "a temporary derangement of the nervous system." According to Boris Sidis of Harvard, who has experimented extensively on frogs, cats, birds, dogs, children, and adults, the cells of the central nervous system, by expanding and contracting, connect themselves with, or cut themselves off from the whole nervous system, and induce "waking-states and sleeping-states." The purely scientific man is forever aiming to reduce all the phenomena of human life to a simple formula. But no formula has yet been discovered which includes all phases of life to the satisfaction of all its students. Hence we have so many different theories of so natural and universal a function as sleep, none of them perfectly satisfactory even to their discoverers or inventors, and none affording any great help to those who want to know how to sleep.

This whole neuron theory, as it is called, of dilating and contracting is really no more complete an explanation than any of the others. No perfect explanation of any natural function can be given until we can fully explain life. That has not yet been done. The most advanced biologists can say, "Here life appears," but they cannot absolutely define life any more than they can create it out of inanimate things.

We know, however, that in sleep, sight, nearly useless to man in the gloom of night, goes first to rest. Next taste goes. Then smell, still so useful to animals, deserts us. Then touch is dulled. Last of all, the hearing relaxes its guard, though with some persons it stays long awake. Noise will arouse us quicker than a touch; and last the light.

As you drop off to sleep you can notice the decreased sensation in the long-serving feet which feels as if it slowly climbs to the muscles in the head and neck.

CHAPTER XXIX
STILL MORE THEORIES

Sleep sits upon his brow;
His eye is closed; he sleeps, nor dreams of harm.
LONGFELLOW.

W E have not yet exhausted all the theories, nor shown how much too much some of them and how far too little all of them prove.

The two remaining scientific theories of sleep are the psychological and the biological. The best modern exponent of the psychological theory is Marie de Manacéïne, who defines sleep as "the resting-time of consciousness." Persons whose consciousness is but little developed, young children, and those of weak intellect, usually require a great deal of sleep, while persons whose minds are active, alert, responsive, get along with comparatively little sleep.

For a long time it was believed that living creatures devoid of consciousness would not sleep at all, but recent experiments have apparently weakened that conclusion. Dogs, pigeons, and other animals deprived of brains in the interest of scientific discovery, appear to sleep, that is, they have periods of inactivity, just as those with brains and consciousness. Belmondo, after repeated experiments, drew the conclusion that sleep is not a purely cerebral function, as some believe, but that the whole organism sleeps; and the brain sleeps only because the organs of sense sleep. This, however, is doubtful.

And this is in sum and substance the biological theory of sleep, that the whole organism sleeps, but even here there are exceptions. It is true that the heart beats less rapidly; that we breathe less frequently; that the brain cells cease their functioning because the neuroglia contracts and shuts off or lessens their joint activity; the motor consciousness rests; the nerves of sensation refuse to be stimulated, we sleep. Yet we know that the spinal cord never sleeps, that certain functions of the body continue uninterruptedly in the sleeping-state as in the waking-state, and, after all these years of theorizing and experimenting, we do not know definitely what sleep is. We know the mechanism of sleep, its manifestations and its effects; we know that continued sleeplessness means madness and death; that sleep is essential to the physical and mental well-being of the human organism, but we do not know what sleep is any more than we know what life is. There is a limit to what material science can know.

Heubel, who is one of the recent supporters of the psychological theory of sleep, says that "Mental activity depends on the incoming peripheral sensory stimulations; when such peripheral sensory stimulations are absent, mental activity is in abeyance and sleep results." This is, in effect, to say that, when things about us no longer give us any sensation, when they do not attract or hold our attention, we fall asleep. But we all know of exceptions to this rule. We have seen others fall into "a brown study," and have probably done so ourselves, and become perfectly lost to all about them; absorbed in their own reflections, they neither hear nor see the things happening around them. For the time being "peripheral sensory stimulations" are absent, and yet mental activity continues and sleep does not result.

The biological theory of sleep considers all the other theories, while formulating its own, because biology considers the whole organism and not only one organ or function of the body. From a different point of view Binns' theory is confirmed by Claperède, who points out that, "biologically regarded, sleep has its significance not as a passive state, but as an active instinct, like all the other instincts of animal life." There is a degree of satisfaction to be found in this theory. It might be stated in this way, that, when man has had during any period all the sensations and experiences he can digest, the instinct to sleep takes possession of him. It is not that he becomes helpless in the hands of those experiences, but that his whole nature, like his stomach, knows when it has had food enough, and desires time for digestion and assimilation before it takes in more. Obviously, "utter separation from the phenomenal world," as John Bigelow expresses it, becomes necessary.

In his lectures on Botany at the Royal School of Medicine in Great Britain, Professor Leo H. Grindon said: "Man is captured in sleep not by death but by his better nature; to-day runs in through a deeper day to become the parent of to-morrow, and to issue every morning, bright as the morning of life, and of life-size, from the peaceful womb of the cerebellum." This is the result not of a passive state, but of an active instinct; it accepts sleep as a time of growth, not merely a time of rest. Bigelow says, "Something goes on during sleep which is a preventive as well as an antidote to mania," and, in furtherance of this same idea, Dr. J. J. G. Wilkinson of the Royal College of Surgeons of London, argues that it seems "as if a reason more perfect than reason, and uninfluenced by its partialities, had been at work when we were in our beds." Even "biologically regarded," Bigelow is not far astray when he claims that "our desire for sleep is manifestly designed to promote in us the growth and development of spiritual graces." In other words, we desire to sleep, that we may relate the experiences of our every-day active life to the sum of knowledge we already possess by inheritance and past experience, that we may thereby get a fuller understanding of life and its purposes.

"It is not uncommon for those who have no habit or inclination to sleep during the morning hours of secular days, to be overcome with somnolency in church soon after the devotional exercises are begun, and to find it impossible to derive any edification from them until they have lost themselves for a moment or two in absolute unconsciousness. Then they have no difficulty, sometimes a lively pleasure, in attending to the exercises which follow. The worshiper is then withdrawn from the familiar excitement of customary avocations. It is idle to suppose that in these few moments of repose, upright in his pew, he has rested enough, in the common acceptation of that word, to repair any waste of tissue that would explain the new sense of refreshment that ensues. He has received, in that brief retirement from the world, some reinforcements which manifestly are not dependent upon time or space for their efficacy—spiritual reinforcements, and spiritual reinforcements only. He has removed himself, or been removed, further away, out of sight or hearing or thinking, so to speak, of his phenomenal life, and nearer to the Source of all life." This explanation may or may not be true. He adds:

"It was quite a common impression among the ancients that sleepers in temples of religion were more apt to receive divine communications there than elsewhere." ("Mystery of Sleep," John Bigelow, pp. 94-95.)

CHAPTER XXX
WE LEARN TO DO BY DOING

Sleep winds us up for the succeeding dawn.
YOUNG.

GOOD health and good sleep are so interdependent that it is as difficult to separate them into cause and effect as to determine "which came first, the hen or the egg?" If it be true that life may be wonderfully prolonged as soon as we have learned to avoid disease and exhaustion, and that we may learn to avoid both by avoiding excess, then it is as much within our power to live long and well as to sleep long and well, if we so wish. Senility, the disease of old age, is now believed to be caused by germs which flourish in the waste matter left in the system through improper or excessive eating.

Metchnikoff, the noted bacteriologist, alleges that the large intestine is the breeding-place of these destructive germs. A Dr. Hall arrived at the same conclusion earlier and combated his germs with copious water-flooding of the bowels. So far, Metchnikoff's experiments point to the conclusion that lactic acid destroys them. That is why he recommends the use of pure buttermilk and has invented a tablet that, dropped into milk, will convert it into a wholesome drink for adult man. Discoveries and inventions of this sort are of great interest to all who enjoy and seek to prolong life. But purely physical things cannot take the place of the mental attitude. The youngest woman of seventy-nine that I have ever known is one who says, "Tell me more; I must not get into such a rut that I cannot grow." No discovery or invention will do us much good if we allow habit to cramp our thought and custom to stale it.

Science may show us how to avoid disease and to prolong life, but, if we turn a deaf ear to her teaching, we shall get no benefit from it. It is the alert, open mind that profits from discovery or experience. The sun may shine with life-giving power, but, if the house be shuttered and darkened, it will not benefit the dwellers. So with the mind. If we resolutely shut it against new ideas, if we refuse to take even the gift of life and health from an unaccustomed hand, then we must expect to suffer.

If we would rid ourselves of sleeplessness, of disease, and dissatisfaction, we must be willing to let go of every habit, every thought, every feeling that may injure us. To hug them to us is merely to invite further suffering, to lessen our own vigor and our own enjoyment.

Nevertheless, we must hug our habits to us, if we can see or understand nothing better. No one can help us beyond what we are willing to receive: anyone can lead a horse to the water, but no one can make him drink. If the end in view seems to us worth the price we must pay, we pay it. We have no choice; for our desires push us that way. We often take credit to ourselves for things for which no credit is due us. However self-denying an act may seem, it is, after all, the thing we want most to do, else we would not do it.

In the same way, if we refuse to profit by the discoveries and experiments of others, if we prefer to go on in our old way of suffering, nobody can really prevent us. It is all a matter that we must decide. This book does not pretend to cure any ill. It intends merely to show what investigation and experience have proved; to point to possible ways of escape from the ills with which men now suffer. If it looks desirable to you, you will only read it; but, until you have tried it, you cannot say whether it is good or not.

CHAPTER XXXI
VAIN REGRETS

Thou hast been called, O Sleep! the friend of woe;
But 'tis the happy that have called thee so.
SOUTHEY.

SOMETIMES we lie awake at night to regret some action of our own because the result has not been what we desired or expected. "John the Unafraid" says that "if your misfortune is not your own fault, you have much to be glad of. If it is your own fault you have more to be glad of, since you can prevent that misfortune from occurring again." In either case, therefore, you may follow the advice given so many years ago, "Rejoice evermore." At least it is evident that in neither case need you lose sleep over it: for, according to your light, you did what seemed to you at the time best for you to do.

For, to quote Epictetus again, it is not possible "to judge one thing to be best for me and seek another." The thing you did, you did because it seemed best to do that, and to regret now and wish you had done something else is, in reality, to wish that you had been a different person from what you were, which is a foolish regret, or, that you had done something different from what seemed best to do. That would be a mild form of insanity. You don't really regret that you were not insane?

It has no bearing on the case that the outcome has proved that you were mistaken. You might never have learned that your course was not best for you or for others, except by doing just as you did. Now you have that much more knowledge than you had before, and you can use it to help you another time. A man can't do any better than he can. You cannot do more than you *know*, and you only know what you have learned by experience. The great majority of us learn only in the school of personal experience; the few wise ones learn some things through the experience of others, by relating or applying their own experience to the events in the lives of others.

Comparing and reflecting, they come to see the close relation of act and consequence, and thus recognize the universal laws in operation.

Such wisdom may be yours, but it will not come through regretting that you did not possess it ready-made. Besides, no misfortune, whether we are ourselves directly responsible for it or not, is ever in vain. No matter how hard and almost unendurable the "misfortune" may have seemed at the time, we shall find in looking back that it was no unmixed evil. The terrible calamity has often been the turning-point in our lives. It made us pause and think, and, through the thinking, we have achieved development of which we were otherwise incapable.

Even when we do not always see this for ourselves, partly because we are not always good judges of our own development or progress, we see it plainly in the lives of others. A friend of mine once said to me of a woman who was doing a tremendous work in the world, "I remember when she was just a selfish society woman." "What changed her?" I asked.

"Oh, she lost her only daughter very suddenly. It was a terrible blow, and her friends thought she would never recover. But she did, and those who love her best know that that heavy sorrow was really a blessing in disguise. Think what she is now!" I smiled appreciatively, for my friend was herself still smarting from a keen disappointment which she had not yet recognized as a blessing in disguise. But recognizing it in another's life must eventually help her to see it in her own.

If our misfortune has come from a selfishness that we might have overcome, and did not, we shall not better matters by wasting time in regret. "Repentance"—which is the only emotion such a misfortune should arouse —"is to up and act for righteousness, and forget that you ever had relations with sin." Unless we "bring forth fruits meet for repentance," our repentance is lost, and we are indeed worse off than if we had felt none.

Spinoza, the Jewish philosopher, has spoken almost the last word on the uselessness of regret. He says: "One might perhaps expect gnawings of conscience and repentance to help to bring him on the right path, and might thereupon conclude (as everyone does conclude) that these affections are good things. Yet when we look at the matter closely, we shall find that not only are they not good, but on the contrary hurtful and evil passions. For it is manifest that we can always get along better by reason and love of truth than by worry of conscience and remorse." It is an old Hebrew idea that we should repent in sackcloth and ashes, making ourselves miserable that we may make God happy. We forget that love cannot enjoy anyone's misery. It were indeed a perverted mind, whether human or divine, that could derive pleasure from the discomfort or sorrow of another.

Plants grow better when the sunshine warms them, and human beings expand and develop under the sunshine of joyous reflection and effort. If you are losing sleep through dreary or hopeless regret, purge your mind of such folly, and, after a sound sleep, you will find that things look brighter.

There are, of course, exceptions to the rule that sleep brings mental quiet, for some sorts of nervous sufferers are prone to depression in the morning, but it is not common among active, healthy persons. They, like well-nourished children, awake to find each day a fresh delight.

Dr. M. Allen Starr, the distinguished nerve specialist of New York, writes me that there are several explanations of the cause of such depression. He is of the opinion that those who are depressed from melancholia when they wake in the morning, are probably suffering from a toxic condition of the blood which originally produced the melancholia. This toxin, or poison, is resisted by the nervous system when it is well nourished, but has a greater effect when the nervous system is poorly nourished. He says that there is a general consensus of opinion that, during sleep, the blood vessels of the brain are contracted slightly so that the amount of blood going into the brain during sleep is less than during the waking hours. This was proved many years ago by Professor Mosso of Turin, by a series of experiments which are conclusive. When blood vessels are contracted, and less blood is going to an organ, the nutrition of that organ is less actively maintained. Hence, if a person has poison in the system, it is less restricted during sleep, has a greater opportunity to attack the nerve-cells, and thus to prevent the nutrition which is essential to the feeling of general comfort. That is the theory on which we physicians explain depression on awaking after sleep in melancholia. What is true of melancholia is probably true also of fatigue conditions and irregular conditions of health, many of which are dependent upon the existence in the blood of substances detrimental to health, either the products of indigestion or the poisons of disease. This theory explains the conditions in which a person not actively ill may awake from a sleep in a state of depression. (See Appendix A.)

Prof. Edward M. Weyer in reading the sheets of this book suggests another tentative explanation of depression upon waking: if we consider the nerve cell as stored with energy, then, if the store is maintained at normal, it is in a healthful state. The supply fluctuates somewhat during the day, but in the melancholic person it does not rise to normal even after good sleep: the less amount of carbonic acid gas eliminated during sleep leaves the system on waking at the mercy of that poisoned gas and of the chronically low nervous energy.

CHAPTER XXXII
THE LOVE THAT IS PEACE

Sweet gate of life, sweet type of death—
    Come, Sleep!
        DORA READ GOODALE.

MANY persons lose sleep because of their love for others, as the lover who sighs and tosses, dreaming, asleep or awake, of the beloved. The mother loses sleep thinking of the child with its little worries and problems, its willfulness or its frail health. There is always some cause that seems to her reasonable ground for worry. The father, too, plans for the future of his son, and lies awake to map out a life for another human being, as if that being were a puppet and his father held the strings by which it could be moved in his hands.

Dickens showed the futility of such planning in "Dombey and Son," and we have all seen it in actual life. Yet we go on doing as our fathers did, and suffering, as we say, "because of our love." It is really only because we do not understand what love is.

What we usually call love is largely self-love; that is why we hear so much of the pangs of love. Love, being the essence of godlikeness, ought to bring us the joy of the gods, and love would bring only joy if we could forget ourselves. We understand ourselves so little that we do not know when our love is self-love. We are always seeking some return upon our affection, as if it were an investment that must pay dividends to prove its profitableness. The price of our love is generally the right to criticise, to influence, to control; or, if we forego these seeming advantages, we expect at least consideration from those whom we have blessed with our love. No relation of life seems too sacred to escape the contamination of the selfish demands of self or narrow love.

The mother loves her child, cares for it in its helpless years, gladly risks even her life for it, and yet may be unwilling that that child shall live its own life, follow its own yearnings, think its own thoughts. The great stumbling-block of the parent is the unconscious demand for gratitude, the claim made upon the child of a return for the effort and affection so freely bestowed. It may be that the parent does not look for material returns, such as money or position, nevertheless a price is exacted every time that the parent is surprised, disappointed, or angered by the child pursuing some course contrary to his teaching. The love that cared for the helpless child becomes the tyranny that would control its thoughts and action.

We say "This is natural," but we seldom say, even to ourselves, "This is selfishness." We would not desire to compel another to think as we think, if we were not sure that we could not be mistaken. It is a conceit of ourselves which makes us quick to thrust upon another "ready-made" opinions because they are our opinions.

But there is a still more subtle selfishness than this that may be at the bottom of things. If we have earnestly advocated anything which the world has been slow to accept, we feel that it is a sort of attack upon us and our views when our children do not support those views. We say, "How can we expect others to heed us, if our own children don't heed us," and so we are hurt or angered. We think of their opposition as disloyalty, and it does not occur to us that it might be no advantage if others did heed us; that the very opposition of our children may be the best means of preventing us from doing harm to our fellows.

Besides, if we cared more that men should see the right and love it, than that they should heed us, it would not hurt or vex us whether they listened or not. If we have a message, it will find hearers and followers. "There can never be one lost good," says Browning, and, if what we would teach is good, it will find its own. It is self-love, not love for others, which makes us sore or angry when they will not listen.

It is a narrow love that makes us fail our friends because they have not fulfilled the ideal we had of them. We never really loved them. We loved something that we thought they should be, and were unwilling to find them something different. We get pain out of our relations with our fellow-beings because our love is not big enough to exclude self.

We make in our minds a model of what our friends should be, and it takes up so much room that we cannot accommodate so much as a mental photograph of what they really are. And just there lies not only the possibility but the absolute assurance of "disappointment" in them, and consequent "pain" for ourselves.

If we knew our friends for what they really are, and were willing that they should be themselves, we could not possibly be disappointed in them. We really insist upon our friends being in "our own image and likeness." Just so the Hebrews, in the efforts to present God to the world, made of him simply a man like themselves—big and strong, to be sure, with sentiments of love and pity and justice, but with a lust of anger and revenge which almost blotted out his tenderness. Many people still cling to this idea of God, but they are mostly those whose love is so full of self that even the Supreme Being must conform to their standard or they cease to believe in him.

The "disappointment" that so often follows marriage, even between the fondest lovers, is mainly caused by this narrow or self-love. Most married misery is due to each trying to improve the other instead of himself. "Because I love him," says the wife, "he should do as I ask him, but he refuses. He does not love me as I love him. I am almost broken-hearted with disappointment." "Any wife who loved her husband would find it a pleasure to be and to do what he asks. My wife does not conform to my wishes, but insists upon doing as she herself prefers. If a man is not the head of his own house, how is happiness possible? Marriage is indeed a lottery, and I have drawn a blank," says he.

But there is one thing certain, if we find ourselves suffering through our love in any relation of life, whether as husband or wife, mother, daughter, lover, friend, we may be sure that it is because our love is not broad enough; because we believe in ownership, or desire gratitude, or are confident of our wisdom and ability to control the life of another. In short, that we love self best. "Love suffereth long and is kind; ... seeketh not her own, is not easily provoked, thinketh no evil." The largest love embraces, understands, and forgives everything, and knows no disappointments and no end.

CHAPTER XXXIII
THE SPECTER OF DEATH

O FTEN we are anxious and sleepless only because we are afraid of what is not in itself frightful. Like the little child in the picture who mounts the dark stairs in deadly terror of an imaginary bear, we are afraid lest we should see a vague something that might terrify us still more.

But perhaps there is a real specter in our path? Let us attack the most terrible foe; having overcome him, we shall find that the lesser ones have no power over us.

A man was once walking alone a lonely road on a dark, misty night, fearing every sound and looking for danger. He had been told that the road was haunted and this was the terror that possessed him. As he neared the haunted spot, he saw a white form rise from the earth. It was barely discernible through the mist as it waved thin arms and made soft moaning sighs. His hair rose on his head, but his going forward was imperative, so he took heart of grace, and determined to face his adversary.

"Spirit or human," said he, "I shall settle you before I leave this place to-night." With this he dashed forward, and found that it was merely a slender birch with white under-leaves upturned in the wind, as the breeze sighed through its branches.

The rest of the road held no terrors for him. The specter he had most dreaded proved to be nothing at all. In conquering his first emotion of fear he had vanquished all terror.

Maybe we fear the possible death either of ourselves or of some other dearer than ourselves. Are we afraid of that? Let us look calmly at it. Changes have taken place, and are even now in progress in our bodies, yet we do not fear them. For the most part we are even unconscious of them: a change is not terrible in itself, no matter how great it is. Death is but another change, one that has not yet come.

A pious man once appealed in distress to the late Rev. Dr. John Hall: he said he knew his soul was saved, but he was afraid of dying. Dr. Hall asked him, "But you are not dying now, are you?" "No," he said, "but I know that I must die some day." "Ah, well!" replied the doctor, "we hardly need dying grace until our dying day." "As our day so shall our strength be"—the bravest soldier may be nervous contemplating the battle, but in the action he finds not only courage but exhilaration. So, if we learn to live from day to day, we may well put off fear of death or dying until our dying day has come, and then we may find that there is nothing to fear. For the present, what we have to consider is life, and what it may mean.

There are two ways of looking at life: one regards life as the changes that take place in the body from birth to death. The body is always changing, being almost all renewed at least every seven years. Old hair is constantly falling out, to be replaced by new; we cut the excess growth of the nails, and rarely stop to think that the nails we have to-day are not the same nails we had a few weeks or months ago. We get rid of dead skin, and our skin constantly renews itself, and so we feel no worry if we cut or scratch it. We say quite complacently, "Oh! it will heal up and new skin grow." The whole body fades and is renewed. It is not, then, the changes in the body that we fear.

We accept this series of physical changes as physical life, for we know that, if the changes stopped, life would stop also; but we must also recognize them as death, for the beginning of each new stage is the death of the previous stage. Thus death is steadily going on in ourselves, at the same time that life continues, and we not only have no fear of it, but are unconscious of the process: our body is constantly passing from death to life, as well as from life to death, and we are not afraid of that; in fact, we never give a thought to it.

Even from the physical standpoint man need not spend his best years fearing death. When we live so that death shall round out a long life, we shall have lost all fear of it. When we say that a person did not die a "natural death" we usually mean that he died suddenly and violently. But death from disease is not "natural" either, and in as far as we learn how to live aright, harmonizing the physical, mental, and spiritual natures, realizing that the perishing body is not all of us, we can avoid most of the fruitful sources of disease. As we learn what true life is, and how natural the eventual dissolution of the body is, we shall cease to tremble at it.

Metchnikoff, the eminent philosopher and student who has devoted years of study and research to the life and death of man, says: "When diseases are suppressed, and the course of life regulated by scientific hygiene, it is probable that death will come only at extreme old age. When death comes in its natural place at the end of the normal cycle of the physical life, it will be robbed of its terrors, and be accepted gratefully as any other part of the cycle of life." He thinks, in fact, that the instinct of life may be replaced by an instinct of death. "It is even possible," he says, "that the approach of natural death is one of the most pleasant sensations in the world." Perhaps the most striking evidence of the truth of this so far recorded is the case of Brillat-Savarin's aunt—who, at ninety-three, said to her famous nephew, "If you ever reach my age you will find that one wants to die just as one wants to sleep." All of us know of cases where the very aged, having lived their lives to the best of their perceptions, awaited death willingly and almost joyfully. As Browning says, "Thou waitedst age; wait death, nor be afraid." Fear of the approach of death disturbs us because we feel further possibilities of life. We do not want to be cut off in the flower of our existence; we think of death, not as a change of existence, but as the end of it, and we think there is no sure way of avoiding that. All of us have felt the truth of Dickens' idea of the bells which toll almost gladly for the aged, but seem to weep when the young die. We are sure we should not fear death, nor be unwilling to die if we had the privilege of living to a "ripe old age." For time is not measured by the clock or by the calendar; those measure only the revolutions of the earth and of the sun. Time is measured by thought and act, and, more than all, by feeling. And we can ordinarily prolong our own lives to the time when we shall willingly and gladly lay them down.

This willingness is by no means the same feeling that prompts the useless and unmeaning exclamation, "Oh, I wish I were dead!" The average person gets into such an unreasoning state over every little happening that he cannot see any connection between the events in his daily life. He becomes discouraged, and thinks for the moment that he would like to quit it all. No matter how many years such an one has lived, he has not attained a "ripe old age." Ripeness has no part in petty impatience; it implies mellowness, soundness, and general wholesomeness of character.

As man is learning more and more about his life, he is finding that sickness, premature old age, and untimely death are, in a large measure, due to his own misunderstanding of the purposes of life. It is this misunderstanding that gives the mysterious air to life. We fear the mysterious, for our ingrained habit of regarding things that we do not yet understand as insoluble mysteries is a relic of the days when savage man found mystery and danger in everything.

So, if we are making ourselves unhappy, losing sleep, and suffering physical and mental distress because of the possible approach of death, we may dismiss that cause of worry. As soon as we begin to consider the purposes of life and our relation to them, we shall naturally avoid excesses in eating; live as hygienically as possible; harbor cleanly, uplifting thoughts, helpful to others and to ourselves, and so reach out spiritually for a fuller understanding of the purposes of all life. And what we cease to fear for ourselves, we soon cease to fear for our other selves.

Living thus, we shall not fear death, but shall move toward it without thinking of it, knowing that it is natural, merely the long sleep of the objective consciousness.

> Sleep till the end, true soul and sweet!
>   Nothing comes to thee new or strange.
> Sleep full of rest from head to feet;
>   Lie still, dry dust, secure of change.
> TENNYSON.

> O'er each vain eye oblivious pinions wave,
> And quench'd existence crouches in a grave.
> What better name may Slumber's bed become?
> Night's Sepulcher, the universal Home,
> Where Weakness, Strength, Vice, Virtue, sunk supine,
> Alike in naked helplessness recline;
> Glad for a while to heave unconscious breath,
> Yet wake to wrestle with the dread of death,
> And shun, though day but dawns on ills increased,

That Sleep, the loveliest, since it dreams the least.

BYRON.

CHAPTER XXXIV
A NATURAL CHANGE

THROUGH generations, perhaps for hundreds of thousands of years, custom has ordained grief for the dead, we have come to feel that it is a proof of affection or of sensitiveness or a sort of virtue: we indulge in the luxury of woe, we nurse our grief until, like a spoiled lap-dog, it becomes a burden. But we know that the unselfish dead would only be distressed at our grieving.

When we look upon the change called death as no more mysterious than any of the other changes in our bodily or mental development, which we either welcome or are unconscious of, we shall lose our terror of it either for ourselves or for others.

Our terror for others is not really for those others so much as for ourselves. The sense of "our great loss" is really a piece of selfishness. For life cannot mean one thing for us and another for our brother; as we see our own lives, so must we see the lives of those we love. The purposes of life are the same for all men, for all men are in the plan of the Spirit.

If for any reason our brother has passed from our earthly cognizance, we cannot say that we have really lost him. It is true that we do not see him with our eyes or touch him with our hands, but we have a remembrance of him in the form of a mental picture down to the minutest details of how he looked and moved, and we also have a remembrance of his spiritual character.

For the character—that sum of the abilities of those we love—remains with us after the physical form has passed away. We are affected by it just as we were when the loved one lived. We can feel the appeal that that character makes to us, its effect upon our thoughts and actions, as strongly as if the absent one stood beside us and claimed our attention. How, then, can we say he is lost?

The dead whom we have loved hold us as securely as they did when they were living; it is only that we do not see how. It has come within the experience of many that the death of father, mother, or some dearly loved one has led to the awakening of some wayward or misguided one who seemed to be wasting all the opportunities of life. We know that it was not the mere death which worked this seeming miracle. That simply woke the dormant love in the one who had hitherto desired only his own way. As soon as he became conscious of his love for the beloved one who has passed out of his earthly life, he longed to be what his beloved would have had him be, and so he turned his attention to using the opportunities of life, to the end that he might grow and develop. Thus in death the loved one held the wayward friend even more securely than he ever had in life.

We shall not fear death, even for those we love, when we have realized that it is but a passing from life to life—just as the falling leaves do not mean the annihilation of the life of the tree, but merely the end of one phase of that life. Somewhere, some time, that which was really our loved one will blossom again in the world's experience, and even now is continuing to live through its influence upon our lives. "There is no death; what seems so is transition." The bodily companionship with all that it implies, that we have lost: yet, if our beloved had gone to be Viceroy of India, we should miss him, but we should not put on mourning for that, nor "grieve" that we had lost his companionship.

"But we could write and hear from him and so keep in touch with him." True: it is then for your own loss that you mourn.

Nearly all the suffering that death causes us is for ourselves. It is our feeling of helplessness, the emptiness of the earth that is left, the changed world that we look at in the sleepless hours of the night, or, when we awake in the morning, our pity for our own loss and the seeming uselessness of what remains of our existence. This consciousness of our loss numbs us so that we cannot get a realizing sense of the joys of the spirit set free from the limitations of the body. Our love is still so earthy that it demands fleshly as well as spiritual communion.

So real is our suffering when those we love best are torn from us that for a time we are inconsolable. Philosophy, religion, the affectionate ministrations of those about us, avail not to bind up the broken heart. There is but one cure for such grief—to minister to others. Unselfish devotion to a great cause—the cause of our fellows, whether in the mass or individually—is a sovereign balm for a bleeding heart.

When we understand life we know this, for we have learned that neither in joy nor in sorrow can any man live to himself. Action of any sort relieves tension and suffering. If we bottle up all our sympathy for ourselves, it becomes so tainted with selfishness and narrowness that it loses its healing qualities. But if we let that sympathy go out freely to others, forgetting our "personal" needs, it blesses them and blesses us.

A friend of mine lost a son and daughter by drowning, just as they had entered young manhood and womanhood, and for a time his grief threatened to crush him. He found no relief until he had his attention called to the sorrow of another who, through a train wreck, had lost his only child. Although a stranger to this stricken father, he sought him out and, because of his own double loss, was able to comfort him as no one else could. Moreover, the restlessness went out of his own heart; he realized his kinship with all sufferers as never before.

There is a story in "The Light of Asia" that Buddha, to comfort a mother broken-hearted over the death of her only child, sent her to get black mustard seed from a house where death had never been. The mother carried her dead babe about the village, and in each house she was offered mustard seed, but each giver said, "Death has been here." At last she realized that she was not the only sufferer, that death was a necessary accompaniment of life as shadow is a necessary accompaniment of light. Her grief, she saw, was but a part of the common sorrow. The recognition that either joy or sorrow is common to all increases the healing sense of unity, it is a "touch of nature" that "makes the whole world kin." There is no wrong in our grieving, if it comforts us: but to look thus each for himself dispassionately at the cause and the nature of his grief, will surely give so clear a view of it that it will no longer deprive us of sleep.

Then why lose sleep worrying about what we know to be merely a change?

CHAPTER XXXV
THE DISTRUST OF LIFE

Come Sleep, O Sleep! the certain knot of peace,
The baiting-place of wit, the balm of woe:
The poor man's wealth, the prisoner's release,
Th' indifferent judge between the high and low.
                              SIR PHILIP SIDNEY.

I F there is no cause to fear death, even when one views life as purely physical, there is still less cause to fear it when one holds the second possible view of what life is—the view that life is the Unseen Consciousness and is within one's self. These are two opposing views; it is only when we try to combine them that we find ourselves filled with fears. When we reason about our bodily life, thinking of ourselves as animals, and apply the conclusions to our lives as men, we find confusion, uncertainty, and fear: for our minds reach conclusions that our hearts tell us cannot be true.

What man fears is not death—*as an animal* he does not know or see death. As long as a man is mainly animal he suffers only as an animal. The deer that flees before the dogs is not afraid of death, for it is not possible that it could conceive of death: that is possible only to the reflecting and comparing mind. He fears the suffering that must follow from an attack from creatures of superior strength and fierce appetites. So man fears that his animal existence, which he does know,—with all its changes,—may be painfully cut off. As a rational being, man knows that death is only a natural and never-ending change. He knows that life is only that which he recognizes as humanness in himself when he meditates upon it. He says to himself, "I feel my life, not as I have been or as I shall be, but I feel it thus: that I am, that I never began anywhere, that I shall never end anywhere." According to this view, death does not exist.

His animal view of life, as the changes in his body, differs so much from the spiritual view of life as Unseen Consciousness, that he cannot reconcile them. They lead to "warring in his members," a conflict between the limitations of the mind and the intuitions of the soul. This causes fear.

There is, of course, a merely physical shrinking from death, the result of race inheritance. In the early days of our race, before man had learned to control the forces of material life, those men or races of men that did not love life, feared death and avoided it, made less effort, and took less care of their lives, and, accordingly, soon ceased to exist. Only the hardy survived. The fear of death helped to preserve the race.

But this inherited shrinking from death is not what tortures man. What causes the uneasiness is rather that superstitious fear of death, which is really fear of a life after the throes of death. We have made this present life so unreasonable and so inconsistent with our own nature that we feel as if any life after death must be just as incomprehensible and inconsistent as this one, so we fear it. We fail to see that all life goes on developing and improving, and so we think our future life may be much worse than what we have now; then, like Hamlet, we ask is it really "better to endure the ills we have than fly to others that we know not of?" Because we hold these two views of life, the animal's view and the spirit's view, we seem to hear two voices crying in our hearts when we consider things: the voice of the Body and the voice of the Soul. The Body says, "I shall cease to be, I shall die, all that I set my life in shall die." The Soul cries, "I am, I cannot die, I ought not to die," and, as if from still deeper depths, comes an appalling whisper, "Yet I am dying." (Tolstoy.)

It is because of this contradiction that terror seizes the mind when we think of the death of the flesh. Man has so long assumed that his fleshly life is the same as himself that he cannot easily rid himself of the idea. Yet, if a man lose a hand or an arm or a leg by accident, he does not think that part of his consciousness or self is gone. He knows that a part of his body— through which himself is made manifest to other men—is gone, but he does not for a moment think that he, the human being, is any less. And he is not.

It is true that the automatic processes of his mind refuse for some time to accept the loss of the members of his body, he misses that way of expressing his will. But that is not so strange as it may at first seem. All voluntary motion arises from desire, and is sent out from the directing mind by means of the nerves to the part of the body fitted to perform that motion.

We are not conscious of sending an order to any nerve center when we wish to put one foot before the other in walking or to use our fingers in writing.

Yet such an order is given, and the desire and the nerve center have both learned from repeated experiences just how properly to direct that message to the foot or to the tips of the fingers. If, for any reason, we miscalculate, we find ourselves walking haltingly or stumblingly along; or our fingers do not move the pencil fairly so as to get the right results. So, too, when we have lost a foot or a hand, the nerve centers send out their messages with the same force as before, but the messages find no way of being delivered. But at no time does a man think that he is less himself because of the missing member. For myself and my body are not one and the same. *Myself* is that which lives in my body, and neither that body nor the years it exists in any way determine the life of myself. This self of mine, which thinks and feels, is older than recorded time; why, then, should we think that it will end with the century? It would not be possible, within the few years that the body exists, for the intelligence or consciousness of the individual to begin at nothingness and attain the degree of development of a human being.

This self or consciousness is really the outcome of the impressions, experiences, and conclusions of my ancestors for thousands upon thousands of years back, and this self began to be shaped even by that from which man sprang. It is continuous; just as it began before my body was formed, so it must go on after the body ceases to exist; it cannot be a mere part of the body which will change with it or end with it.

We do not know, as yet, how we shall continue to live after the body is laid away: whether in the thoughts and feelings and deeds we have done in the flesh; or in our unending, though unconscious, influence; or in the lives of the children of our bodies or of our minds and hearts. But we do know that the world will never be the same as if we had never been here. We do know that what has existed through unnumbered ages will not end in this.

Life does not cease with sleep nor end with death. "I never was not," says the Bhagavad Gita, "nor shall I hereafter cease to be."

CHAPTER XXXVI
REST AND SLEEP

O Happy Sleep! that bear'st upon thy breast
The blood-red poppy of enchanting rest.
ADA LOUISE MARTIN.

O NE of the main purposes of sleep is to secure rest to men. But intelligence will find rest in many other ways independent of sleep or of promoting sleep. We are just beginning, under the leadership of such people as Miss Eva Vescelius, to make a full use of music as a soother of the nerves: yet, as long ago as the time of David, some persons knew its value. Browning's magnificent poem, "Saul," recounts its force.

As David exorcised Saul's evil spirit by the skillful harp and voice, so those who are studying the therapeutics of music are now helping the physically and mentally ill. Miss Vescelius and those working with her claim that "music is capable of great life-awakening energy.... The use of music for healing the sick is therefore a natural use of a natural power. Music, like medicine, has been divided into classes as stimulants, sedatives, and narcotics. It is now admitted that music can be so employed as to exercise a distinct psychological influence upon the mind, the nerve centers and the circulatory system, and that by the intelligent use of music many ills may be cured." For almost all of us "music hath charms to soothe." Others again find in some form of massage a sweet though artificial sedative; some even in the combing of the hair, which is possibly connected with an electric effect, for we know little definitely as yet of the principles of the possible curative force of electricity.

Others again rest by a mere mental change in their ordinary avocations. My wife was once talking with Mr. Stiegler, a well-known riding teacher in New York, and he said that he was in the saddle every day from six or seven in the morning till eleven at night, with only short intervals for meals. "It's a hard life," he said.

"But Sundays?" the lady asked.

"Oh, Sundays! I have Sundays to myself." "And what do you do on Sundays?" "Oh!" he said, "I take a ride in the Park." The relief from the strain of watching the pupils and their horses was rest to him.

When Weston had won his first six days' walk in Madison Square Garden, he went out to take a walk on Fifth Avenue on the Sunday.

To find harmony with our own natures, to act in accordance with our natural or acquired tendencies, is rest. A peaceful surrounding is rest in itself, though sleep may not be wooed. One may be rested by a walk in a country lane, when a walk in the bustle of Broadway would only tire him the more.

And this peaceful surrounding may be interior just as well as exterior. Mrs. Elizabeth Burns Ferm, who has a playhouse for children on the East Side in New York, and does a great deal of other work, recently said: "I could never accomplish what I do if I did not sleep so well. That rests me completely. I do not dream nor stir. I drop into the homogeneous, forgetting myself and becoming just a part of life. In this way I rest." The oldest books show that, ever since there have been any records of man, he has been seeking happiness and rest, yet he has not attained either happiness or rest. But the seeking has helped in his growth upward and progress has been his reward. As Browning says:

"Progress is man's distinguishing mark alone;
    Not God's; not the beasts': He is; they are;
Man partly is and wholly hopes to be."

Even though man seeks in wrong directions, he is sure to move onward so long as he continues to seek, for, if we sufficiently desire any goal, we shall eventually find it. "What d'ye lack? quoth God," says Emerson, "take it and pay the price." Jesus put the same thing in another form. Said he, "Ask and it shall be given you; seek and ye shall find; knock and it shall be opened unto you." Those who misunderstand life and its purposes apply this only to what are called religious matters, but those who see farther into life know that it applies in every way. It all depends upon what we feel that we lack. If we feel we lack pleasure, or happiness, or rest, we seek them along the lines we think they may be found. And we pay the price that is asked. We cannot avoid this so long as cause and effect follow each other.

If we seek happiness through selfish gratifications, we pay the price of disappointment and pain, if we are at all enlightened. Of course, if a man lives the life of the animal merely, cutting himself off from any recognition of the claims of his fellows, he may get all the happiness he can understand through self-seeking. But the price he pays is that he is not able to understand or to appreciate more than this lesser happiness. As Walter Scott says:

> "For him no minstrel raptures swell.
> Proud though his title, high his fame,
> Boundless his wealth as wish can claim;
> Despite those titles, power and pelf,
> The wretch, concentered all in self,
> Living shall forfeit fair renown,
> And, doubly dying, shall go down
> To the vile dust from whence he sprung,
> Unwept, unhonored, and unsung."

This is the price he pays.

If we seek happiness through the happiness of all; if we forget self, understanding that all are One, seeking that wisdom which comes only from seeing all life as one, we, in like measure, get the reward.

Men, mere animal men, who understand nothing but self-seeking, may speak evil of us, they probably will, but even that cannot "hurt" us. We shall understand that such evil speaking is the best they know, and that, therefore, it is not evil to their minds. Moreover, the further premium to us will be a broader understanding, a deepening love, an increase of happiness, an influx of peace, a pervading sense of rest, and quiet sleep.

This is a premium most of us would be willing to work for, did we but see it. And we may see it if we will. If we ask of life that we get into harmony with its purposes; if we seek diligently even into our own hearts for those purposes; if we knock at the door of man's full life, we shall find our asking answered, our search rewarded, and the door wide open. What a man desireth most, that, somehow, somewhere, shall be gain. Desire creates function.

And, when the soul has gained what it sought, we shall find beauties and virtues hitherto unsuspected in every human being; we shall learn that, above the turmoil and noise of our rushing, jarring, modern civilization, we can hear the morning stars sing together for joy, the music of the spheres, that which shall yet soothe man's fear and teach him to find restful sleep.

CHAPTER XXXVII
THE NEED OF REST

The bliss of an unbroken sleep.
THOS. W. PARSONS.

To go in the wrong direction delays our journey and brings fatigue, but that fatigue may teach us needed lessons.

Man seeks happiness through outer things, hoping to find it in wealth, excitement, travel, self-gratification, and in countless other ways that the age-long experience of men have proved to be ineffectual; but he usually forgets that the wellspring of happiness is within. Long before Solomon had announced that "this also is vanity and vexation of spirit," men had observed that riches do not bring happiness; that excitement wearies us, that travel is unsatisfying, and that gratification of the senses ends in exhaustion.

At last, in despair of satisfaction in the world, we have accepted the teaching that there is no rest on this side of the grave. We have even learned to glorify strain and the strenuous life as natural and desirable. At best, men have thought of rest as something that concerned the body, and have confounded it with sleep and inaction.

If we think we have important work to do, we say, "We have no time to rest," as if any work would be laid upon us that ought to prevent us having rest. Draught horses have been bred for centuries for the sole purpose of work, yet a wise driver never overloads nor overworks his horse. He sees that it is comfortably housed, well fed, and has its needed rest. Shall we think that the Spirit of Life has less consideration for man than man has for the horse? That were in effect to say that man were greater and wiser than that which caused man, and which man has spent the ages trying to understand.

When we stop to think of this we can see how foolish it is, but we seldom stop to think until something "happens" that stops us. We go on from day to day thinking that we have no time to rest. This state of mind, which leads to trouble, is possible only because we do not understand what rest is, nor how easy it is to have it. We ordinarily seek rest only after we have become exhausted.

When we have wearied ourselves with worry, useless exertion, and fretting, or with envy, hatred, or malice; when we have bent all our energies to some low aim or selfish purpose; when we have broken nearly all of Nature's laws and are called upon to pay the penalty, we seek a physician. A man sets a shifting standard of wealth as his goal, and strains to attain it; he eats improperly and in great haste, his thoughts filled with the problems of the market; he is forever on the alert for any advantage that he may take of his fellows; he cannot endure to have another reap an advantage that is denied him; he is envious of every bit of success that, passing him by, goes to another; he makes of his life one fierce round of money-getting. Then, perhaps before attaining his goal, perhaps after reaching it, he discovers himself a physical wreck, and hastens to his physician, seeking external means to cure that which has its root in internal conditions; asking the man of drugs to "minister to a mind diseased." To the nervous, worried, hurried person, from whatever cause, the physician's advice is generally the same —"Take a complete rest," meaning thereby that all work be given up and inaction take the place of activity. When circumstances allow it, we try to follow this advice, but it usually results in boredom and impatience at the lost time; when circumstances do not allow the inactivity, we get discouraged and complain of life as a series of mysterious, unjust happenings. The physician's advice proves a mockery and we become listless and discouraged.

We hardly ever seek our rest from moment to moment; for we continue to look upon it as something we shall find after our work is done. The laborer, the merchant, and the professional man think of the end of the day as resting-time, just as the busy housewife does. It matters not how much we may love our work, we expect to be exhausted by our efforts before the day is over. We feel hurried, anxious, fretted, and overworked all day long, and comfort ourselves with the prospect of rest at night. And all the time we might rest and never find the day so short as to cause worry, nor the hours so long nor the work so hard as to tire us.

It is only when we are burdened with distracting cares that we get tired by what is a joy to us. The true artist wants no eight-hour day; he laments only that daylight fades so soon. When we are doing only what we love to do, and doing it well, we run and are not weary, we walk and do not faint.

Of late years the trainers of athletes have recognized this—they think it more important to keep the men buoyant and fresh than to increase the muscles at the risk of bringing them "stale" to the day of contest. They insist that the men shall not exhaust themselves at any time before the race.

Exhaustion shows either that we have been doing the wrong thing or doing it wrong, and kindly Nature reproves us with the loss of Sleep.

CHAPTER XXXVIII
SAVING OF EFFORT

Rocked in the cradle of the deep
I lay me down in peace to sleep.
EMMA WILLARD.

THE unsatisfied longing for rest in all mankind will be attributed to different causes according to the way we look at life. The physical or animal man desires rest because of the relief it will bring to nerves and muscles wearied by the strain of activities; he feels that to relax will bring him some ease and that relaxation will help him to forget the bodily weariness. Recovering from weariness or pain is a pleasure in itself. The sigh of relief is really a sigh of pleasure.

When the mind reigns, it instinctively recognizes that rest would restore the balance disturbed by feverish exertions. Our whole lives seem passed in a struggle to attain something, and the law of rhythm, which is the law of action and reaction, requires that, after struggle, effort should cease. One implies the other; neither effort nor true rest can continue steadily. Effort is the breaking of rest; shadow is only the relative absence of light.

It is contrast that makes sensations; the shadow serves to make the light brighter; the night makes the day more fair; and noon makes the night darker. Tennyson recognized this in the line, "Sorrow's crown of sorrow is remembering happier things." He might have said, with equal truth, that the present joy has a warmer flush because of forgotten pain.

Wagner understood that, and so we find crash and seeming inharmony so often a prelude to the softest, tenderest strains. The mind first wearies of monotony, even of harmony, and then ceases to be able to perceive it. Wagner saw this, and introduced clashing sound that seems like discord until we feel its connection with the emotion and the context of the piece. These relieve the emotions and throw the harmonies into relief. Says Hobbes: to have one sensation and to have it continually would be to have none.

The mental man feels and knows all this, and to him rest becomes necessary to restore that balance of things that contrast suggests—rest after effort, peace after turmoil.

The spiritual man goes still deeper into true conditions in his longing for rest. Rest carries with it the idea of attainment. He who has attained has peace: "Peace I leave with you; my peace I give unto you." The unity of all three desires—that of the body, that of the mind, and that of the spirit—cannot fail to strike the thinker. To cease to strain is the keynote of ease. Why? Because man sees, however dimly, that agonizing, like antagonizing, is really futile, and that the only thing that is necessary is to put one's self in harmony with the Universe.

Herbert Spencer has shown that grace of movement consists in the economy of effort, in doing every act with the least possible waste of power. The same thought is the basis of the teaching of the great Delsarte. As Ruskin says: "Is not the evidence of ease on the very front of all the greatest works in existence? Do they not say plainly to us, not 'there has been a great effort here,' but 'there has been a great power here'? It is not the weariness of mortality, but the strength of divinity, which we have to recognize in all things; and this is just what we now never recognize, but think that we shall do great things by the help of iron bars and perspiration. Alas! we shall do nothing that way, but lose some pounds of our own weight." The best way to attain anything is to move towards it with the least possible jarring or friction. In every struggle we lose force, because we are sure to make unnecessary motions. Men do not learn this from their daily work as unconsciously as they once did, because machinery has so largely displaced handwork. But, even in using machinery, he is the best workman who has learned to run his machine and get good results with the least expenditure of physical effort. Such a workman remains fresh for a longer period, and accomplishes more in a given time. The machine itself is constructed upon the principle of saving effort—it cuts out all unnecessary motion and reduces friction as much as possible.

If you watch a skilled typesetter at his case, you will find that apparently he is never in a rush. The beginner, especially if he is one of the more nervous type, looks anxious, pauses with hand fluttering above the case while he considers in which box he will find the letter he seeks; then, when he has made a decision, he will pounce upon it and deposit it in the stick with breathless haste. Not so the seasoned compositor. There is no haste, no fluttering, no waste motion. His hand goes unerringly to the box where he will find the letter he wants, in a twinkling it is in place in the stick, and another letter disposed of in the same way, and you are scarcely conscious of motion. The perfect workman is he who has learned to accomplish most with the least expenditure of effort. It is toward this perfection that Frederick W. Taylor and others are striving in the new "Business Efficiency." Every day we are surprised to learn that what *we* gained by hard struggle has been gained with scarcely an effort by another. It does not always make us happy to learn it. We often feel as if we had been tricked, and we think that effort spent in what we now see was not the most effective way, was wasted. This leads us sometimes to persist in a mistaken course, because we are unwilling to believe that we have lost so much time and missed so much result. But no effort is ever wasted: it is only by the effort to do well that we can learn to do better.

Nothing is commoner than to hear our friends say, "I don't sleep—the work is so hard and exacting I get dead tired and then toss about all night." But it is not the work, rather it is the worker that is exacting.

CHAPTER XXXIX
ANTAGONISM

Lord of the Darkness, Master of the Sun,
Strip me of all my strenuous life has won,
But let Sleep's sweet oblivion o'er me sweep,
Closing Night's leering eyes—oh, give me sleep!
Anonymous.

THOUGH you want rest, peace, sleep—the opposites of strife—yet people will oppose you and want you to go their impossible ways. That need not arouse opposition, nor break your rest, nor disturb the even tenor of your way. One disadvantage of allowing ourselves to be disturbed is that we cannot be angry with one person without being angry with all about us. Or at least the harmony of our relation is broken, because, despite our effort, we cannot succeed in separating ourselves from our brothers. The next time you are angry or impatient with someone who has opposed you, take note how it affects your tone and your feeling toward those who are innocent of any offense.

One such investigation into our own condition when annoyed will help to cure us of being angry; for there is no use in trying to correct all the mistakes or worrying over the neglects of others, even of the children of our own bodies. Other people, "the same as us," have to learn by their mistakes, and often do learn by some success that we considered manifestly impossible.

As we could not be wisdom and conscience to the whole world, Providence has kindly given us enough to do in taking care of our own actions.

When Mosenthal was organist at Calvary Church, the brides used to give him directions about just what pieces they wanted played at their weddings; Mosenthal would say, "Ah! that is a beautiful selection," or "A magnificent march!" As he said, "I listen to all the lovely ladies' orders—then I play what I think best—and it always goes all right." He did not make rows by trying to convince excited girls that the "Mikado" would not be just the thing for the church, or to persuade nice mammas without musical education that "Traumerei" would not do for a wedding. It was not necessary to lie, only to give what approval could be given and then to "gae his ain gait." Most people are not really much set in their own ways, they only seem to be. They have an idea (or they think they have one—an idea is a rare and precious possession) and they want to "get it off." Let them; why should you make the explosion dangerous by confining it? Maybe they were only trying to argue with themselves, and, having got rid of the idea, they are content, if their self-love is not roused in defense of it. Like the codfish which deposits her eggs and has no more care about them, they are quite content to leave the results to Nature.

There was a tract called the "Oiled Feather," which was very popular in England forty years ago. Sam, a wagoner, has a bottle of oil with a feather stuck in the cork, and, when a barn-door sticks or harness creaks or a king-bolt binds, instead of using force, he always brings out his oil bottle and feather. His friend has not learned the usefulness of gentle methods and gets into all sorts of trouble, until he sees that the Oiled Feather principle applies to horses and to people and to difficulties, as well as to things.

"Est modus in rebus"—which means that "there is a way in things" just as much as in people: get into key with it and all will go smoothly. Did you ever try to split trap-rock with a hammer? You may batter all day at one side and you will only knock off chips, spoil your hammer, and hurt your hands: but, when you have found the right spot, a tap knocks it in pieces. That tap is the "open sesame" to which alone the stone will yield. You may storm at it all day with your "open millet" or "open wheat," but its heart can be reached only by its own word. So the stony heart of the world can be broken only by the Master Word of Love.

Now, if you have made what is said in Chapter xxvii your own, you do not need all this; for you know that, as long as you arouse antagonism in others, you can be annoyed and irritated by others, but not one moment longer. The punching-bag can neither dent nor be dented: if it is so made that it injures no one, it turns out that no one injures it, no matter how roughly he strikes it.

When your lovelight shines in darkness, not only will your own path be bright, but you will be a guide and a comforter to others, and they will follow you.

CHAPTER XL
STRUGGLE IN THE FAMILY

How happy is that balm to wretches, sleep!
BEAUMONT.

I F all that we have learned were that some persons "naturally" work harder than others to achieve anything, we might say that this was unavoidable; and there would be a degree of truth in it. It is true that the intelligence of some people is so sluggish that they learn little from experience. They continue to work towards any end in the same way that they have always worked, wasting both strength and time. For them there is nothing but repeated experiences and patient guidance until they learn to apply their knowledge practically.

But the intelligent man learns that, often where he has worked in the hardest possible way, he has had the most unsatisfactory return for his effort. The good housekeeper, for instance, wishes above all things to make her family comfortable; she has inherited a feeling of the requirements of healthy living, and decides that she must have a scrupulously clean house to protect her loved ones from the dangers of germs and microbes.

So she sweeps, scrubs, cleans from morning until night; carefully removes every trace of dust, follows her family with dust-pan and brush, and at least looks reproachfully at the offender who does not remove every trace of street or garden dirt from his shoes before entering the house. She cleans so hard that she forgets that the real object of cleaning is to make her family safe and comfortable. They may be safe, but they are a long way from being comfortable, and she knows no more comfort than they; cleanliness has become a fetich with her, and some day, perhaps, she comes to her senses, finding herself chasing the motes in a sunbeam, lest by chance they should rest upon her sacred furniture.

If she then sits down to take stock of things, she finds that husband and children almost dread to come home. However serene and happy they may be before reaching the garden gate, or the apartment door, they then become nervous and distrait. They look themselves over, to be sure that nothing is amiss, for "mother is so particular." An anxious expression settles upon their faces, for, with their best endeavors, they may have overlooked something that mother's trained and suspicious eye may note. The joy of life abates, and a sort of painful hush falls upon things.

The average child cannot see that this condition grows out of misdirected love and care; he sees no connection between it and his well-being, but, if he thinks of it at all, he concludes that "the house" counts for more with mother than anything else. Husband and children unconsciously come to regard her as mainly a housekeeper, with interests bounded by the four walls of the home. The very gifts they make her are of a useful nature —"something for the house"—as if the "house" were some special thing in her personal life but meant nothing to them.

When the hungry heart of this woman pains her, she resents the condition that she herself has created, but does not see the correct remedy. Her husband and children have put her out of their inner lives; they take their pleasures away from home, they find their confidantes among outside friends. Who should share their thoughts and their pleasures? she asks. Who has worked day and night for their comfort and happiness as she has? And the chances are that she considers them ungrateful and herself a martyr, when all the time she herself builds the barrier between them and herself by striving to make them happy in her way. That it is not their way, and so could not be in harmony with the natural trend of things, does not once occur to her. As the French say, "Madam costs herself too much." She has not learned, and may never learn, that the only way to make others happy is to love them sincerely and unselfishly enough to allow them to be happy in their own way.

Sometimes it is the father who destroys the joy of home. A many good men think that their duty is done when they provide food, clothes, shelter, and education for their children, and insist upon obedience from them. They are so busy attending to these things that they have no time to get acquainted with their children, to know or be known by them.

There is too much truth in the newspaper joke on the suburbanite. A mother found her little boy crying bitterly on the doorstep quite early on a Monday morning.

"What is the matter, Freddie?" she asked, anxiously.

"Why," sobbed the child, "I was just running down the street when the man who stops here on Sundays spanked me and sent me home." There are many children who have no cause to welcome "the man who stops here on Sundays," even though he may be counted "a good father." Very often he "takes a nap," and all noise must cease for his benefit; or, he cannot read his Sunday paper while they are playing about. He speaks testily to his wife, blaming her that she does not quiet the children. "They have all the week to play," he complains, "I should think they could keep quiet on Sunday. It is the only day I have to rest, and you ought to see that I am not disturbed." And the mother, who hasn't even Sunday to rest, quiets the children in the only way she knows, and everybody is wretched.

As fast as the children grow up they leave home gladly for college or business, and, though they respect and fear "the Head of the Family," they have no real love for him; they never consult him on their intimate, personal worries or problems, and he many times carries a sore heart behind his seemingly stern manner. He wonders why his children are so ungrateful, when he has spent his whole life toiling for them. In his bitter moments he may even call them monsters of ingratitude; forgetting, as Dickens says, that he is really looking for "monsters of gratitude." These parents, like everyone else, have it in their power to attract to themselves the affection and the surroundings that they need, and to create a center of repose even in the midst of strife; rest we may attain even amid turmoil; but true repose means that quiet shall spread from us to others.

CHAPTER XLI
UNNATURAL LAWS

So many Gods, so many creeds,
    So many paths that wind and wind,
    When just the art of being kind
Is all this sad world needs.

ELLA WHEELER WILCOX.

B UT the harmony of the home does not depend upon the parents alone. If it did, it would forever disprove the statement that it is only by a working together of all parts of any organization that its real purpose may be accomplished. A clock is intended to tell the time, and its mechanism is so constructed that, by its working together, the hands and chime will mark the hours. But, if we could imagine the hands of the clock refusing to move in the direction that the springs, wheels, and pendulum required, and insisting upon going their own way, the usefulness of the clock would be destroyed.

So, in the matter of family harmony, it may be merely some self-willed son or daughter, even a child, that causes the discord. And he is not necessarily a "bad" child, either. He may be endowed with special gifts, and be particularly adapted to give joy to those about him. He loves his parents, his brothers and sisters, and also that intangible "home" that counts for so much in life—yet, because he loves his "own way" more than all else, he makes "home" impossible. He is so sure of his infallible judgment that he opposes every suggestion that does not come from himself; he offers free advice on every possible and impossible occasion; he "takes sides" on every question that arises, and considers any opposition as a personal attack or affront. He is not conscious of these or of any other faults, yet every remark, every act is tested by its possible reference to himself. He looms so large in his own foreground that he cannot see how he could be unimportant to anybody's life or thought. He broods over fancied wrongs and thinks himself the most ill-used of mortals. Everybody is unhappy where he is, and he is most unhappy of all.

For it is a well-established fact, one which we may find proved every day both in our own experience and the experience of other people, that he who makes another unhappy generally makes himself still more wretched.

If our experience shows us any exceptions to this rule, it is, after all, only in seeming. He who can make another unhappy and not be conscious of it, is among those whom Epictetus calls blind in that knowledge which distinguisheth right from wrong. He has not felt his close relation, or, indeed, any relation to his fellows. He cannot know any of the joys of fellowship, and he will not find the pleasure he expects even in his own pursuits. For it matters little, so far as seeing is concerned, whether a man be born blind, or whether he keeps his eyes tightly bandaged all his days. In either case he gets none of the sensations of pleasure that come from being able and willing to see. If we persist in having "our own way," we must pay the price. Most of the miseries of life are caused by failure to get in harmony with the laws of life. This is as simple and self-evident as walking up the street. If we persist in keeping to the left on a busy sidewalk, we shall be jostled and pushed until we are sore and out of breath and make but little headway withal. But, if we are careful to walk with the crowd going in our direction, if we remember always to keep to the right, we shall find it easy to get along even at the "rush" hour. Those who do not observe this rule of harmonious progress not only find walking on a busy street hard work, but they also make it harder for others. One man walking the wrong way may compel twenty more to violate the sidewalk customs to overcome his opposition. But, when everyone observes the rule, it leads to a saving of time and temper and makes life safer for all who are in the crowd.

Generally speaking, we recognize no law but that of our own will, which is by no means the same thing as the far-wider law of our being. We cannot separate our lives from the greater life. While we follow the law of our own will, self-will, we never know real happiness or rest. Like many another man-made law, our antagonistic wills are a perversion of the natural law which governs our lives.

SLEEP'S CONQUEST

Invisible armies come, we know not whence,
And like a still, insinuating tide

Encompass us about on every side,
Imprisoning each weary outpost sense,
Till thought is taken, sleeping in his tents!
Yet now the conquerer with lofty pride
Becomes our guardian, with us doth abide
And plans all night our wondrous recompense.
He takes away the weary, worn-out day,
And brings to-morrow—bride without a stain;
Gives us fresh liberty, a chance to mend;
Life, hope, and friends enhanced with fresh array.
Then when we fail he conquers us again,
Paroling us each day until the end.

CHARLES H. CRANDALL.

(Courtesy of Harper & Brothers.)

CHAPTER XLII
THE NATURAL LAW

B UT what is the law of our being? It is harmony, peace, rest. We have but to look at the workings of our own marvelous physical bodies to perceive that law. The more we study the human body, the more we wonder at its mechanism. Yet every part of this intricate machinery, in harmony with each other part, finds its own work, unless man, through his misunderstanding, throws it out of order.

Perhaps the strongest proof of the naturally harmonious working of the body is found in the responsive distress or disease which result from the wrong use of any one function. It is not necessary to cut the heart itself to injure it. To sever an artery anywhere will interfere with the perfection of the heart's work as effectively as a direct injury to the heart. To bring bad news may stop its action forever.

It is not necessary to strike the head to cause a headache; that will follow if we abuse the stomach, or live so that the liver becomes deranged. We get these results because of the perfect harmony in which all the parts of the body work when we conform to the law of our being. The pain is a kindly monitor, warning us that we have violated some law and bidding us get into line once more. It is always wise to heed such warning, gratefully.

Suppose that a man has a cellar which is so dark and damp and dirty that he hates to go into it, and tries to forget it. But it is flooded in a storm, and he is forced to go down to examine it, and then finds that the wall is unsafe, and must be supported, else the house may fall. Will he not say, "It was well that the flood came that took me down into the depths, so that I might find what was endangering my property and the lives of my family?" And if, in addition, he not only reinforces and buttresses the wall, but also lets in the light and cleans up the cellar, he will actually remove out of his life what was always a disagreeable and neglected task. He will add to the value of his property, and have besides a security in his house that he would never have had but for the "accident." So we, if we heed the first pain that tells us we have violated the law of harmony in our physical body, may be led into a better and truer understanding of ourselves than ever before.

If the law of the physical body is harmony, peace, rest, it must be true that the law of the intelligence and the law of the spirit are the same. If it were not so, there would be constant warring between the three natures—physical, intellectual, and emotional—and happiness and rest would be impossible.

Harmony, peace, rest are the blessings that all men crave, even when they do not understand their own desires. To say that peace and rest are inherently impossible of attainment is to say that we are formed with desires that tantalize and torment us, as a mirage tantalizes the traveler dying of thirst in the desert, with no hope of satisfying those desires. It is in effect to say that a cruel monster governs this world and takes delight in our suffering.

He who tries with apparent disregard of harmony to enforce his own will is, after all, striving in his blind and hopeless way for harmony. He thinks that to make his will supreme would bring peace, and so he tries to have his own way: that accounts for much tyranny, especially domestic tyranny.

That so few do attain happiness and rest in their lives is because of this misunderstanding of life rather than from any inability to gain happiness and rest. We allow trifles to distract us from our real purpose. We feel ourselves so pressed and oppressed by petty cares that we cannot find time during the day to do all that we feel we must do. It would be well for us to follow Pitt's rule, to do our part in the world instead of trying to run it.

If that rule worked in his high and responsible position, it would probably work in our less important places. Most of us spend our strength for that which is naught, largely because we do not examine the nature of the "duty" which presents itself to us. We should probably find that our duties are not worth doing, or else that another could do them as well.

Rest brings sleep more than sleep brings rest.

CHAPTER XLIII
"LETTING GO"

In sleep's sweet fetters bound.
LORD NEAVES.

A FREQUENT cause of suffering among men and women is their idea that they are necessary to the running of things. Usually they find themselves mistaken. The head of a firm was once warned by a physician that he must take a rest to avert a breakdown, but the man declared it to be an impossibility for him to get away from the office for even a week. He gripped his business so tight that he could not let go, nor could he see that others could do it as well as he could. In such a state of mind the doctor's warning added another worry, fear for himself,—so at last the predicted breakdown came. He had reached the point where he had to let go, for his grip, both physical and mental, was gone. For six months he could not concern himself with business affairs, the necessity of fighting for life and renewed health occupying all his faculties. He refused to let himself think of the outcome, but put his attention upon getting well.

When he returned to his business, with his mind braced to stand any disasters that he might discover, he was astonished to find everything in perfect condition, and that his assistant had even corrected the errors he had himself made in the last weeks of overworked body and fagged brain. It was at first a blow to his pride that he was not essential to the success of his own business, but, as he realized how big a price he had paid to learn this simple lesson, he made a decision that showed how far he had advanced beyond his former condition.

Turning to his assistant, he said: "Smith, as you can carry on this business so well, I shall take three months' vacation every year, and have no more expensive breakdowns; and, as I want you to continue to carry it on as well while I am away, you would better take three months' vacation every year, too, so there shall be no breakdowns for you." He had really learned two lessons in one—what things were not worth doing, and what things could be done by somebody else. He still had left "the things that were quite enough for any man to attempt." No man is really indispensable to any undertaking, however much it may seem so to him. When James Alexander controlled the Equitable Life Assurance Society, he made it his rule to discharge anybody who seemed to be indispensable. His reason for this was that, the longer such a man was retained, the more indispensable he would become, until the association would be in danger of going to smash if anything happened to that one man. Common prudence dictated the advisability of getting rid of him while the company could manage to get along somehow without him.

There was once a Dutchman who was of much the same opinion as Mr. Alexander. His manager applied for an increase of salary.

"I t'ink I buys you bretty dear, alretty, Hans." "Yes," said Hans, "I get a good salary, but then I am worth it. I know everything and do everything about the business; in fact, you couldn't get along without me." "Ach, ish dot so? Vell; vat I do if you vas deat, Hans?" "Oh, well! if I were dead, you'd have to get along without me." "Ach!" replied the Dutchman, slowly, "den, Hans, I t'inks we gonsiders you deat." It is well to think sometimes of how nicely the world got along before we came to it, and how likely it is to do just as well after we have left it. If, when we are rushing around, weighed down by anxiety and a feeling of our own importance, we should "consider ourselves dead" for a few moments, we might find that the fever of life had subsided.

We should have to admit that, judging from the past, the world would not even slip a cog if we were to pass from it. And even if we were ready to claim that no one heretofore had been so important, and no one could ever again be so necessary, even then it were the part of wisdom to cease hurrying and worrying. For, as the human frame can be exhausted by overwork and overworry, it behooves the indispensable person to preserve himself as long as possible, so as to save the world from the catastrophe of his loss. The very thing he aims to do—save the world—he defeats by his anxiety and haste.

Proper prudence tends to prevent trouble, not to prevent worry. No amount of precaution and care will cure worry. In fact, the prudence and care help to fix the thought on all the mischances, however improbable or impossible, that may be imagined.

Elaborate precautions often defeat themselves, like a corporal who kept all his squad out as pickets till they were cut off one by one.

I once saw a family going off to the country, five "masters" and three servants, eight hand-packages, coachman, footman, and an extra servant, and the family doctor to get them off. The cautious doctor got the tickets days before, and even got checks for the trunks. An extra trunk, taken at the last hour to hold some extra things that might be needed, upset all that arranging.

The doctor went to the baggage-room in the gray dawn to get that precautionary trunk checked: after a long discussion about the place, he arranged to meet the family at the railway news-stand. The caretaker was shown once more how to work the burglar alarm, from which a necessary knob came off in the nervous hand of the Master of Cares—"telephone for the electrician" but at last the blinds were carefully pulled down, the house shut up and committed to Providence and the caretaker, and the family and its familiars arrived at the station nearly an hour before train-time, "getting off so nicely." The Genius of Forethought sent out a pair of scouts to find the doctor. They returned, to report that there were three news-stands, but the doctor was not at any of them.

Then this Genius of Care went himself with one of the scouts, a long and hurried walk to the baggage-room,—not there.

Meanwhile, the doctor, who had stayed to see the trunks off, had found the main body with its camp-followers and light baggage. All stood in the station near a news-stand and waited for the return of the expedition, till the doctor got impatient as train-time approached and went off to find the Head of the House, who arrived in a flurry, having lost his own head a few minutes after he had gone with the tickets.

At last, after the pilgrimage from the ticket-gate down to the parlor-car, they are in the train, all safe, thank God; but the Genius of Care did not sleep that night "on account of the worry and fuss of getting off." That was not the doctor's fault. Like Martha, he had made his own punishment the same as the rest of us by being *careful about many things.*" I remember an Irish servant who was shown one of our big banks with its huge window-bars, to make it safe. "Sure," she said, "what's the good of them things? The thieves is inside and not out." Worry is inside and not out, and Sleep, like the Kingdom of Heaven, is not taken by force.

CHAPTER XLIV
REST IN TRUTH

The timely dew of sleep.
MILTON.

I T is not our work that wears us, but the way we take it. So long as we think of rest as meaning only inactivity, just so long will the activities of life exhaust us. Goethe said:

"Rest is not quitting the busy career,
Rest is fitting oneself for one's sphere."

When we do that, we find rest. But we may ask what is one's sphere and how may one fit one's self for it? If we wish to answer that truly, we must be willing to have some common misconceptions brushed away. The sphere of any individual is limited only by the possibilities of his own body, mind, and spirit. Our sphere is not a small circle of activities whose boundaries any man may mark. It widens as our inner nature expands, and what was the horizon line yesterday will be but a tiny hillock near at hand to-morrow. It includes all that has been achieved, and all that may be attained by the race.

The best standard of our life is not only what the race as a whole has achieved in the way of development, but the highest and best that any person has yet taught or lived; this is the true measure of man's sphere to-day. Ordinarily, we talk of man's sphere and woman's sphere as if there were a clear line of separation between them, and each were continued in its own little space. This could not be, for, so long as men and women have the same three natures—bodily, mental, spiritual—so long as we have similar needs, aims, and aspirations, the larger sphere of man, whether male or female, is the same, and is bounded only by the possibilities of the life of all three natures.

To fit one's self for such a sphere should bring rest while we are doing it, because that fitting means becoming harmonious with the purposes of the larger life; and rest is simply harmony, at-one-ness with the Universe.

The possibilities of the life of all three natures are inexhaustible. We have never touched the limit of even the physical man. Man at one time had only his hands for tools, and so was limited in his powers. But he used his mind to increase the power of his hands, and reached out for sticks and stones to help him. In time his thought devised implements that increased his physical power a thousandfold, until now he has harnessed not only steam, but the very currents of the air, and is making himself all-powerful.

He does not wholly understand the forces he tries to control, but he studies them, experiments upon them, and makes servants of them as far as he has grasped their laws. Had he insisted upon considering his mind and his physical powers as entirely separate and refused to use them together, he might still have claws for hands, and might still be a mere burrower in the earth. Moreover, his mind would not have developed as it has. Steam and electricity might have aroused his curiosity, but he would not have known how to make them to do his will.

Further, if man had been able to keep his intellect apart from his spirit, he would not have developed the qualities that lift him above the more intelligent animals. Sympathy and justice and love would not have come into his relations with his fellow-men.

These moral feelings expressed in our bodies, our minds, and our hearts are some of the possibilities of the life of all three natures, and to endeavor to know and harmonize them, thus "fitting one's self for one's sphere," would bring us the happiness that follows action and the rest that flows from selfless purpose or harmony.

If we consider what the true object of life is, we cannot help trying to see the connection between the three natures of man. It does not seem possible that the life of any thinking being was intended to be a purposeless jarring jumble, or, as poor Stephen Blackpool said, "a' a muddle." We find such harmony in the life of the material world that we may expect to find a similar harmony in the life of man. So soon as we discover this, we see also that there must be harmony between the life of the material world and the life of man, and further harmony between both the material and the human life, and the Source of all life. Seeing this, and living it, is fitting ourselves for our sphere, preparing ourselves to take our destined places in the Universe as Men and Women.

CHAPTER XLV
THE SPAN OF LIFE

We are such stuff as dreams are made on, and our little life
Is rounded with a sleep.

SHAKESPEARE.

Only a generation ago it was the custom for men and women to begin to grow old at about forty-five. A person of fifty was always called "old," and a man was expected to be decrepit at sixty, a woman much earlier. It is not wonderful that such men begrudged the time spent in sleep.

When I was a boy, we used shamelessly to print books in big type, indorsed "For the Aged," on the theory that everyone must be nearly blind at maturity. Even now Dr. George F. Stevens thinks that everyone "ought" to wear glasses after forty, notwithstanding that many Christian Scientists and Mental Scientists discard them long after that age.

There is as much truth as wit in the saying that "A man is as old as he feels, a woman as old as she says she is." We used to insist upon every year being counted and noted, too, in dress, occupation, and general demeanor. But we have changed all this—even natty dress now common to older people shows it—but the change has come about slowly, and there are still many who think that people of sixty should give up all active life and prepare to "grow old gracefully," that is, to drop willingly into senility. Those who are willing so to slip into uselessness quietly, need much sleep; but even for them the sleep is not a waste of time, but an aid to length of days.

There has been a great deal too much willingness to let go of active life, because of the idea that "threescore years and ten" was the natural limit of man's life, and that to live beyond seventy-five was to live upon "borrowed time." There is a sort of tickle for the mental palate in that expression "borrowed time," but there is no substance in it, if we will but examine it. How can there be "borrowed" time and from whom is it borrowed?

Life is not a thing that begins to-day and ends to-morrow. So far as we know, it has neither beginning nor end. It is beyond our power to picture a limit to all life. Well, if life has neither beginning nor end, if it has no limits, and if time is merely the unit by which we measure seasons, why should there be a limit to what we can use of it, and how could a continued use of it be called "borrowing"?

In the earlier days of the race, when all progress was made through might, and war settled every question, when a man's "work" meant chasing over the hills, when men fared hard, and knew little of Nature; when fear was the supreme emotion—it is probable that seventy years represented a long life. To escape all the chances of death from accident and ignorance for so long a time was an achievement, and, in this way, doubtless, seventy years came to be regarded as the natural period of man's physical existence.

But with our increasing knowledge, with the extension of means for making life easier, with our conquest of Nature, there is no excuse for limiting ourselves or our fellows to the same short span. Consequently man's life began to extend over a longer and longer period as the risks of living were diminished by civilization. War became a less common condition; the very inventions for making war more destructive of life helped to make people consider whether disputes could not be more wisely settled. The next step was a natural outcome of that reasoning. The latest wars have had more casualties and less fatalities; partly because the effort has been to incapacitate the fighting-men rather than to kill them off. We have begun to see dimly, at least, that the taking of life does not settle any question. This leads to a greater respect for life, and from respect to preservation is an easy step.

The intelligent man to-day does not make his whole life a mere struggle to exist for his "allotted span." Rather, he aims to preserve and prolong his life by exertion and, even more, by repose. He has learned that, while it is true that "not enjoyment and not sorrow is our destined end or way," yet to enjoy, in the sense of understanding life and living, is to live so that "each to-morrow find us farther than to-day." To enjoy life is to use it wisely; to get the most out of it that will make for happiness and development. It will not help to that end to worry or lose sleep, because man's span of life is short. Love with your whole heart, and live according to reason, and you will win the prize of sleep, and happiness and length of days shall be added thereunto.

CHAPTER XLVI
WASTE STEAM

I F there is one thing more than another for which Americans are noted, it is "nervous energy." To this we attribute our notable achievements in science, industry, and literature. To this energy, also, or rather to the misuse of it, may be attributed the dyspepsia, the nervous headaches, the general "breakdowns," and the suicides so much more prevalent of late years.

An abundant supply of nervous energy is one of the blessings of life, it denotes almost unlimited capacity for work and enjoyment. It is the steam that drives the engine; and which, under the control of a skilled engineer, pulls the train upgrade as well as on the level. It is only through ignorance or carelessness that the engine is allowed to run wild, and destroys that which it was meant to convey safely.

So with the people who "go to pieces nervously." There has been an unskilled hand on the lever. Through ignorance or carelessness, the nervous energy has been badly handled, and the force that should convey us safely through life has caused our destruction. We should be as careful with our minds as with our machines.

When we find ourselves getting nervous and worried, sleepless, "blue," or dyspeptic; or showing any of the numerous signs of misdirected energy, such as short temper or headaches, we should take a day off to examine the engine. It is time well spent, as we may thereby learn something that will avert a complete breakdown.

If we find that we are not overeating, overworking, or overworrying; not feeling animosity, nor suffering from an excessive idea of personal importance—if, in fact, there are no fears gnawing our heartstrings nor any other large and well-defined cause of trouble, we may well look closer for small causes. "The foxes—the little foxes that spoil the vines."

There are often disturbing causes that we fail to notice as disturbing. For instance, disorder about us, the habit of stirring everything up and throwing everything around when we set to work. The confusion communicates itself to our feelings, besides which the uncertainty as to where we have put what we want next upsets our nerves.

It is a good plan, when we find ourselves "rattled" or not working easily, to stop and clear things up, put everything in order. It is marvelous how often that will smooth out the creases both in face and temper and make the world look pleasant again.

If that itself proves to be a certain strain or an annoyance, leave the whole thing and go out for a while, or take a nap, or even smoke, if you do not feel that smoking hurts you. Anything that will distract the attention from the seemingly annoying circumstances will relieve the pressure on overwrought nerves and allow the system to regain its poise.

At this point it will sometimes serve to put into practice the rule that William Pitt, Prime Minister of Great Britain, laid down for himself: When overwhelmed with official duties, he divided his work into three parts—that which was not worth doing, that which would do itself, and that which was quite enough for any man to attempt. Make a list of all the things you have to do, then go over that list and make it into three. Pick out first the things that could be left undone, because not really worth the effort they require. Having settled them, you will find your load already lightened.

Next select those things that you want to do, but which somebody else could do just as well. Make that list carefully. It is the hardest one of the three. It is comparatively easy to decide that a thing we may wish to do is not worth the effort it will cost, but it is quite another matter to admit that somebody else could do those things just as well.

And there is a reason for this feeling apart from mere ordinary conceit, although it may only be a more subtle form of conceit—self-approbativeness, as the phrenologists call it. It has its rise in our belief that, while our way of doing that particular thing may be no better than another's way, yet it is "different," and we long to see the result of that different way. Nevertheless, it may be that the best good of all concerned requires that somebody else do that thing, and our nervous restlessness is merely a warning for us to omit doing it ourselves.

Then, in the things left on the original list, we shall find all that one person should undertake, and we shall do them with a zest and ease that could not have been ours working in any other way. For myself, when all else fails, and none of these devices does away with the feeling of being pushed by my work, I close my desk and go for a walk. If soothed, I return in an hour or two and take up my work easily; otherwise, I leave it all until another day; it saves time in the end. Circumstances prevent many persons from doing that: but we can do it, in greater or less degree, far oftener than we think.

It is always advisable to stop long enough to find out what is the matter. If a good engineer finds his engine running hard, he examines it to finds the trouble. If your watch goes irregularly, you take it to an expert to find the cause of irregularity. Why should we be less careful with our minds?

What is needed is simply obedience to the laws of Nature that we know, but the case may be one for the physical culturist, for the mental therapeutist, for the moral teacher, or even for the alienist. Where common sense fails or is wanting, we should consult an expert before it is too late. (See Appendix A.)

CHAPTER XLVII
UNDERSTANDING

Enjoy the honey-heavy dew of slumber;
Thou hast no figures and no fantasies,
Which busy care draws in the brains of men;
Therefore thou sleep'st so sound.

SHAKESPEARE.

ALL unrest and uneasiness, all impatience and disharmony are due to some misunderstanding of life and its unity, of its unchanging and unchangeable laws. Froebel's recognition of this principle created his idea of education as growth by exercise, the greatest definition of training that has yet been given to the world. He says that education consists in relating the individual life to the external life, the inner to the outer, or, in other words, it consists in getting the individual into harmony with the whole of life.

This is the substance of the doctrine of all the great thinkers of the world, the essential oneness in the teachings of all the philosophers of every race and of all the ages. Each gives expression to the special side of this oneness that presented itself most strongly to him, but on the plan of life they agree.

Although many of the followers of these great teachers have been able to see the beauty of their conceptions, few have been able to transmit them as pure and bright as they received them. It is by no means easy to avoid interpreting what we hear in a merely personal way. Seldom do the "hearers of the Word" have the humility "of the broken and empty vessel," so well expressed in a hymn at one time popular among revivalists:

"Empty, that He might fill me
As forth to His service I go;
Broken, that so unhindered
His life through me might flow."

Instead of that, we have tried to make the truth fit our ideas of "personal" life, when we should have made our "personal" life fit the truth.

One cannot conceive of the Universe growing weary, of infinity becoming exhausted, because material science has shown us that harmonious laws govern all life. Scientists have been able to state laws that experience has shown to be unfailingly true. For example, take the heavenly bodies: through the study and comparison of their motions, astronomers have stated laws that apply to all that is known of them, and which illustrate the perfection of the solar system. To-day, if some asteroid is discovered which seems to move in opposition to known laws, no one supposes that the laws are wrong. So impossible is any haphazard occurrence in the solar system that astronomers know that any disturbance simply shows some existence or activity not hitherto observed. They do not doubt the unchangeable universal nature of the laws; but they recognize that only lack of knowledge prevents our understanding the relation of what we see to the laws that govern it, and they bend every effort to the solution of the mystery.

If we but look upon the occurrences of human life with the same confidence, there is no cause for worry and uneasiness. Why should man chafe? Because of those who do ill? "Fret not thyself because of evildoers," for they, too, have their uses. Every man is in the plan of God. It may be that he is here simply to show us something that we should not otherwise have seen. Had not someone done the ill and made the results known, many men might have made like mistakes and the consequences have been much worse than they are. Says Ernest Crosby:

> "I thank the kind round-shouldered men
> And treat them with respect
> For teaching me to raise my chin
> And hold myself erect."

No man can tell how much more he owes to the things that he would have made different had he shaped his own life, than to the things he regards as good.

Most advances that we accomplish are forced upon us by circumstances with which we are discontented, and our happiness consists in recognizing that there is, in effect, no such thing as misfortune. There is no chance in the world: everything is the result of Energy; nothing ever happens by accident. I said once to a woman standing beside the coffin of her husband, trying to comfort her and trying to teach myself, "You know, this did not happen by chance." "No," she said, "I know that; if one chance got loose, it would wreck the world." So it would.

You toss up a coin and it seems to you to be chance whether it comes down heads or tails. It isn't chance at all. If one thing happened by chance, you would know that it was the end of natural law. Suppose that the thing to be tossed were an iron plate, ten feet across by two feet thick, then the engineer could figure out just how many pounds of powder would turn it once and how many would turn it twice or three times; and, if you told him when he had adjusted his charge that it was chance which side would come up, he would say that you did not understand dynamics. He knows that there is no chance about it; that the number of turns depends exactly upon the amount of force, and how it is applied. So it is with the tossing of the penny; it may seem to be chance to us because we cannot measure or perceive the causes, but its fall is as directly and fixedly due to causes as the sinking of an ocean-liner.

It is not likely that Charles Dickens would have chosen the hard childhood he had if he could have arranged his own life, but there is little room to doubt that much of his understanding and sympathy, much of the power that made him the novelist of the masses, was due to those experiences. Even though he may never have seen during his life how necessary those experiences were, nor accepted them philosophically, that did not alter their use. The work of the "evildoers" in giving Socrates hemlock to drink did not destroy Socrates' usefulness; the death by the cross did not check the spread of the good news the Nazarene brought to man.

Men have always stoned the prophets and killed those who would bring deliverance. This is an expression of the conservatism which is the balance-wheel of the race: if it were not for that, the leaders of the people would get so far in advance as to be clear out of sight. But the prophecies have been fulfilled, and, step by step, deliverance has been won. Moreover, whom one generation destroyed, succeeding generations have honored; it is impossible to get the rear rank in line with the vanguard. But wherein has evil triumphed or the law of good been set aside?

In the study of history we see the persistent progress of the race. However slow the march, it has always been from darkness into light, from low aims and small ideas to higher purposes and larger thoughts. Each nation has contributed something to the sum of that progress. Not only have they had glimpses at their best of better things, but even at their worst they have caused other nations to see and avoid like errors or cruelties. In this way the civilized and the savage have both helped to advance civilization. And, if the blind works of evildoers do not triumph over the plans of Good, if they do not even hinder the working of the law of universal Good, why should we fret ourselves because of them?

But the unrest may be caused by our lack of that worldly success which we think would bring us happiness. Of course, if the real desire be worldly success, and there is no other way in which we can learn that it will not bring happiness, then we must attain worldly success. To-day, this demands a resolute will, concentration, a steady nerve, and a lack of human sympathy. It is difficult for us to see this in our own case when we make worldly success our aim, but, if we examine the career of any "successful" man, we shall see how true it is.

Nothing is truer of modern business life than that the success of one involves the failure or seeming failure of many. We have but to look around at the few who are acclaimed by the world as successful business men and the many who toil for a bare subsistence, to find the proof of this. To succeed, a man must first resolve to succeed, and must concentrate all his powers to that end. He must have iron nerves so that unexpected good-or ill-fortune may not upset him, and he must so steel his heart that he may not see the needs or hear the groans of his suffering fellows, if to hear or heed would interfere with his purpose.

After men have attained worldly success, they sometimes give liberally to charity and public purposes. Nobody has yet revealed how much of that giving is atonement for the half-remembered times when some heart was hardened, some ear deafened, and some hand tight closed against the cry of the needy. Some rich men unhappily become so hard of heart, so bound by the habit of refusing, that giving becomes an impossibility.

Now worry and unrest upset the nerve, disturb the concentration, and keep alive at least one phase of human sympathy—that which we call irritation. We do not usually regard irritation as an expression of sympathy, but that is just what it is. Irritation towards our fellows is an indication that we cannot rid ourselves of the knowledge that they have claims upon us. It is an evidence that we do not understand them, or that we are not in harmony with them. That may be because their aims are so different from ours that they are a standing rebuke to our selfishness, or because their aims are so similar to ours that they become a threat to us. In either event they are forced upon our attention, and we are unable to forget them. We are not able to crush them ruthlessly if they stand in our way, for to do so causes us pain and dissatisfaction, and prevents our joy in our success. Sometimes, when the pain and dissatisfaction become keen enough, they may even turn us from our purpose, and thus destroy our chance of worldly success.

Thus worry and unrest defeat the very thing we are aiming at, and leave us out of harmony with the laws governing the accomplishment of our purpose. Even in business and in matters of health, that rest which comes from a cool, steady purpose, undisturbed by fretfulness or impatience, is the main factor of success.

CHAPTER XLVIII
THE SUPERSTITION OF FEAR

Fear of Death thus dies in senseless sleep.
BEAUMONT.

PRIMITIVE man feared thunder, and, being unable to explain it, made a god of it, offered sacrifices to it in the hope of averting the harm it might do.

Fear has perverted many religions. What man feared he first crouched before in helpless terror, and afterwards knelt before in wonder and worship. In the early days of the race he looked upon every new or strange thing with terror, because he did not understand its connection with the things he knew.

Man first knew himself as a physical creature with certain needs and cravings that must be gratified if he were to live at all. He did not at first realize that the presence of another person would make life easier and more secure for him; rather, he feared that every other would injure him. Later, as men formed themselves into groups, clans and tribes, each recognized the interests of the immediate group as of supreme importance, but feared the other groups. This was the origin of "Honor thy father and thy mother, that thy days may be long in the land." Those families that obeyed their natural leader, the patriarch, held together and survived; the others were separated and destroyed. The early records of the Jews are scarcely more than a chronicle of the wars of a coherent race against various other tribes inhabiting that part of Asia, together with the lessons to be drawn from its experience. Even in the vast new continent of America, different tribes of Indians roving its plains looked upon other tribes with distrust and hatred, and made war upon them. There was plenty of land; animal life abounded; there was nothing in the aims and pursuits of one tribe that was necessarily injurious to any other, yet apprehension and the superstition of enmity kept them apart.

The world has not yet got rid of this old superstition. In this modern Christian era there is scarcely a civilized nation which does not keep itself in readiness to attack its neighbor. All the peace the nations yet know is an armed peace, so that even when we cry, "Peace, peace!" we know "there is no peace," because man does not yet trust his fellowman. He is fearful of him, not only as encroaching upon his actual territory, but he resents his competition even in the making of the tools and goods that civilized life demands.

We erect tariff walls, that the people of other countries may not easily sell to us the goods they make, forgetting that, even without those walls, they could not sell their goods to us, if we did not want them. For, in free buying and selling, the desire must be mutual, else there will be no exchange.

In all the relations of the most modern civilized society the effect of this distrust, of one toward another, is plain to be seen. Even those who devote their lives to preaching the doctrine of the gentle Nazarene do not always grasp the full significance of that doctrine. The city of Toledo, Ohio, is blessed with a mayor who has lost all distrust in man (or perhaps he never learned it) and, in his efforts to administer civic affairs on a basis of love and understanding, he is finding his strongest opponents in some of the preachers of the community. Such is the blinding effect of misunderstanding the unity of all life.

It cannot, therefore, be a matter of surprise to the student of present-day affairs that his ancestors were slow to learn about other groups what their still earlier ancestors had learned of individuals. As the circle of man's interests enlarged, including more and more fellow-creatures, he began to come more and more into harmonious relations with the Universe. Out of his personal experience he began to perceive the mutual interests and the underlying oneness of human life, and, through that perception, some have now begun to realize the oneness of all life.

This is the road along which man must travel to reach harmony, and harmony is rest. It is living in accord with the universal law which regulates the growth and development of all things as well as their activities. To the undeveloped savage the whole material universe, so far as he could see it, was a jumble of inharmonious and unrelated things—he saw no relation between the different bodies in the heavens as they circled in their orbits; each created thing seemed to have its separate existence, which had to be maintained without regard to any other form of life. But science has shown us that the heavenly bodies, however huge or remote, are all parts of one great system, under one perfect law. We know now that, instead of the earth being the center of the universe, round which all the stars, suns, moons, and other bodies revolve, it is itself but a tiny unit in a tremendous system of systems.

All of these bodies have been circling in their orbits for untold millions of years, unaffected by the fact that no man knew of them. It is not too much to expect that they will continue to perform their circlings according to those same laws even after science has taught us all it is possible to discover. Man may profit from his knowledge of universal laws, but he cannot alter them.

And yet the man of average intelligence even to-day feels that things universal in relation to humanity and its needs are at "sixes and sevens," and that his anxiety and feverish activity are needed to alter or better them. He still sees men as separate beings with interests that clash.

It is this failure to understand that every life is bound up for good with all other lives which leads us to worry about our "personal" affairs, and thus to miss the rest that clear understanding would bring.

CHAPTER XLIX
IMAGINARY FEARS

O soft embalmer of the still midnight.
KEATS.

WHEN we learn to confine our attention to "the things that are quite enough for any man to attempt," we shall find that there is little real ground for worry or fretting in our daily life. It is a fact that, if our work wearies or exhausts us, either we are doing the wrong thing or else doing it in the wrong way. For the Spirit of Life is no taskmaster. It is we who make this world a daily grind. It is not naturally a "vale of tears" nor a "wilderness of woe."

"Joy upon joy and gain upon gain
    Are the destined rights of my birth,"

and we may all have those rights if we claim them as our own. Worry is a disease that some people enjoy as much as some others enjoy invalidism. There are some people who can hardly speak and think of anything but their physical ailments; they never recall the mornings when they felt strong and vigorous, the nights they slept soundly, but only the days when they had uncomfortable sensations of weakness or distress, and the nights when sleep was somewhat broken. And you will notice that they will say they "did not sleep well" when they mean that they did not sleep much. We may always sleep *well*, even though we do not sleep much.

There are other people who, though they do not weary us with accounts of their bodily symptoms, tell us always of their cares. They revel in tales of distress which shall go to show how much more oppressed they are than their fellows. They take their worries as the healthy farmer takes his food, eagerly, and would be distinctly upset if anything happened to interfere with their enjoyment of them. If they are going somewhere, they worry lest it should rain, or lest something unforeseen should happen to prevent the expedition. It is the same old story, they want their "own way." They cannot conceive of a disappointment being a blessing in disguise; they know of nothing so hard to be borne as the setting aside of a passing desire.

For such as these life is full of "bitter disappointments"; cares and worries naturally fall to their lot; the sun seldom shines for them, and even when it does they think they can note the spots upon it,—while the rain falls so heavily and so frequently that it makes runnels over their whole plan of life, reducing it to a scene of desolation. And all the time the sun is shining, and joys are awaiting them did they but look in the right direction. They are "pulling the wrong string," as it were. A little child kept calling to his mother that he could not find what he was seeking, because he could not "make the light come on." His mother wisely replied: "You are probably pulling the wrong string, Harold. Pull the other." The moment he did so the electric light flooded the room, and the child found what he sought. It had lain right to his hand all the time, but he did not know to pull the right string. Our heart's desire lies just as close to us.

Many a person who is always having trouble, who is worried and uneasy, longing for rest and comfort but never finding it; to whom "life is a dreary puzzle scarcely worth the solving," is simply "pulling the wrong string," the string of self-will, of separateness. His soul is darkened by his refusal to turn on the light, and the shadow covers the whole of his life.

The darkness is filled with imaginary terrors. We people the corners with hobgoblins that do not exist, and that in our hearts we know could not exist. Little Bessie had for several nights cried out in terror after she had been put to bed, so that her mother was compelled to go to her. At first she would not say what had frightened her, but at last the story came out.

"I was thinking how frightened I should be if there was a bogey-man in the closet and he should suddenly put his head out and make faces at me." "But, child," said her mother, "you know there is no such thing as a bogey-man, so he could not be in the closet, nor make faces at you." "Yes, mother, I know that," answered the child, slowly; "but, mother, *if* there was a bogey-man, and he did get into my closet, and if he did put out his head and make faces at me, wouldn't I be awfully frightened? Well, it's *that* that makes me scream." And often the thing that makes us "scream" has no more existence in fact than Bessie's bogey-man. We get to turning things over in our minds, dwelling upon dire possibilities until they become actual to us, and we get as much pain and suffering from them as we should if they were real.

It would puzzle ourselves, if we gave the matter attention, to discover why we are more given to worrying than to rejoicing, if it is not that we misunderstand life and its purposes.

Consider life just on its physical side, and we shall see, as the Creator saw when he looked upon it, that it is all very good. There are more sunny days in the year than stormy ones; there is more growing time than decaying time, for spring, summer, and autumn comprise three parts of the year, and growth continues through them all; the moon shines always somewhere, and "the stars come nightly to the sky." The bright-colored blossoms show more than the somber-hued; more birds sing sweetly than croak harshly, and even the croak melts into the symphony as a needed note. The purely material world points to joy and gladness rather than to sorrow and repining.

Then, when we come to man, we find that he has more strength than weakness, more health than sickness, more power than inability, else man had not survived the ages. Moreover, man must have more capacity for enjoyment than for sorrow, else he would abandon life in weariness, or at best he would forget how to laugh; the mere animal does not laugh, that is one of man's accomplishments.

Man has also more desire for knowledge than for ease, else he would never have penetrated into the secrets and mysteries of Nature; man's strong aspirations surmount his groveling tendencies, else he had never come up out of savagery into the light and development of kinship with the high gods.

Then, why should we give way to repining? All things point to the apostolic truth that "Weeping may endure for a night, but joy cometh in the morning." And always the morning comes. Moreover, the darkest night is seldom starless if we look up intently enough. If we blind our eyes with tears, we cannot see the light even when the horizon is rosy with the rising sun. Better by far is it to feel with Browning:

"How good is man's life,

The mere living! How fit to employ

All the heart and the soul and the senses forever in joy."

CHAPTER L
ILL SUCCESS

"And comfortress of Unsuccess
To wish the dead good-night."

KIPLING'S "True Romance."

IF we aim at worldly success, thinking that thereby we shall be able to do more for mankind and be more useful, we may defeat our own purpose by worry and anxiety. The present moment is all that any man has in which to come into agreement with his fellows.

If for lack of understanding he spends that moment in worry and unrest, he makes himself and everybody else more or less unhappy, thereby destroys his own usefulness, and proves his unfitness to gain success. But it may be that he is deceived as to his motive; he may desire success really for the satisfaction of winning against his less fortunate fellows.

Why should we desire worldly success to enable us to help our fellows? No amount of benevolence or philanthropy can atone for the selfishness, inhumanity and the greed necessary to acquire great wealth under modern conditions. The widow's mite or the cup of cold water given from moment to moment is of greater value than the millions bestowed upon charity as a sop to one's conscience, or as a pacifier of public clamor.

There is a degree of satisfaction in giving *all* that can never come from giving a portion of superabundance. We never hear of a very rich man giving all that he hath, over and above a comfortable, or even a luxurious, living. His giving hardly requires the sacrifice of even a whim. How can a man like Rockefeller, with an admitted income of nearly a dollar every second, be generous? How much would he have to give in order to feel it? —and what mischief would he not do in giving such a sum! The "luxury of giving" can never be his, for that is the result of giving at the expense of our daily desires. The widow who cast in her mite enjoyed the luxury of giving, and many still give in that way. This gift of somebody's mite incited the giving of millions.

But it is not possible that the gift of millions should bring the giver much happiness, if it brings any. There is too much publicity and display in such a gift; it is noised abroad from press and platform, and creates a new distress in the mind of the giver. The giver knows that unscrupulous, undeserving persons or causes will now lay siege to a share of his wealth, because of the notoriety his great gift has brought him. Some are so oppressed with appeals that they have to appoint committees to give away the money. There must be about as much satisfaction in that as in having a committee to kiss the women you love.

Besides this, great benefactions cause uneasiness, lest they be misapplied or unwisely distributed, or lest the glory may be eclipsed by some other millionaire giving a larger sum to a more popular cause. Thus donations become a source of unrest and worriment, and the donor's last state is worse than his first. The giver of the mite is generally unknown of the crowd, sometimes unknown even of the one to whom he gives, so that his joy comes from the giving, and cannot be taken from him. To him alone is it true that "the gift is to the giver" and that "it is more blessed to give than to receive." If there is no real joy to be had from giving of great wealth, why should we desire to have it, or fret ourselves that we do not win it? Neither to acquire wealth nor to possess it can bring happiness or peace. We have seen how great is the price we must pay to get great riches, and it is easy to see why their possession cannot bring peace or happiness.

Man has a limited number of wants, and there is an end even to whims. When all of these have been satisfied, what is left? The ordinary man must give time, skill, thought, and labor to satisfy his needs, and from the effort he gets a large measure of joy and satisfaction. Even if he never gets what he is after, the effort has given him pleasure, strengthened his purpose, and developed his whole nature. But the wealthy man is denied this natural satisfaction. He does not even have to seek what he wants; servants do that for him; he speaks and the thing is done. For him there is no joyous effort; no increase of pleasure in the very delay of fulfillment; no sense of achievement when he gets what he desires. For this reason he soon wearies, and, having run the whole gamut of pleasures, and exhausted his idle fancies, he becomes a prey to ennui, has no object in life, and finds no delight in the days. It could not be otherwise. As an old servant in my family once said, "If the rich were happy, we should know there was no

God." "How hardly shall a rich man enter into the kingdom of heaven," said Jesus; meaning thereby that the possession of wealth destroys our sympathy with our poorer brethren and prevents a man from seeing his true relation to those who have it not; makes it difficult for him to recognize his oneness with all mankind, and so cuts him off from that heaven of love and peace on earth that can come only from agreement of his own life with the life of others outside his circle.

If we are worried or ill at ease for any other cause, such as ill-health, disappointed affections, unsatisfied desires, or from any of the innumerable causes to which we attribute our ill, we have but to examine them to find that in every instance the underlying error is the same. It is that we think of our separate interests, that we are for self; that "me" has a deeper significance to our mind than "us" that the "I" blots out the "thou." All worry, all unrest comes from self-seeking, from the feeling of separateness rather than of oneness; from an inharmonious attitude towards life and its underlying verities.

"Seek ye first the kingdom of God," said the Teacher, "and all these things"—material things, food and clothes that he had been speaking of —"shall be added unto you." Now God is love, and the kingdom of God is universal love, the love that knows no separateness; therefore let not your heart be troubled, neither let it be afraid. Believe in God. The man who seeks first the wide Universal Peace does not worry nor fret. He has, by that very seeking, put himself in tune with the Infinite, and he finds that the sounds which have seemed to him like harsh discords are, to his listening ear, blended into harmony. He has heard the "sweetest carol ever sung" and nothing can drown its melody. With that song in his ears he can "run and never be wearied, he can walk and not faint." He loses his feverish impatience, for "he that believeth shall not make haste"; he sees himself in every man and every man in himself; he has found rest for his soul.

When this peace reigns within, the seeming ills of life do not disturb us. We are not conscious of ungratified desires, and in this lies the truth of the promise—"all things shall be added unto you." For, if man is not conscious of any ungratified want or desire, then, though he be poor in this world's goods and entirely unknown, he is richer by far than the multi-millionaire who is compelled to heap silver upon gold, or the pushing politician whose thirst for fame can never be slaked. He is in harmony with the Universe, he has allied himself with moral gravitation, and, going with its force, he is upheld and supported, so that he has rest now and is neither worried nor afraid.

CHAPTER LI
SOCIAL UNREST

Peace, peace, thou over-anxious, foolish heart;
Rest, ever-seeking soul; calm, mad desires;
Quiet, wild dreams—this is the time of sleep,
Hold her more close than life itself. Forget
All the excitements of the day, forget
All problems and discomforts. Let the night
Take you unto herself, her blessèd self,
Peace, peace, thou over-anxious, foolish heart;
Rest, ever-seeking soul; calm, mad desires;
Quiet, wild dreams—this is the time of sleep.
LEOLYN LOUISE EVERETT.

INQUIRY into the causes and the cure of sleeplessness leads us inevitably to one conclusion: there must be peace of mind, harmonious action and interaction of mind and body in order to command the most refreshing sleep. A man may not know which of the many theories of sleep is correct —indeed, he may not know that there are any theories about it, but, if he lives a normal physical life and is at peace with the world, he is likely to sleep well.

Since health of body, mind, and soul is essential to our best development, and since sleep, restful sleep, is essential to such health, it would seem that such sleep is one of the things which rightly belong to every individual. And, if to individuals, then to groups of individuals, to nations, to the whole race. The race is subject to the same influence as the individual, and, since the chief cause of the unrest of individuals is their inharmonious relations towards one another, so the chief cause of the unrest of the race is its inherent discord.

Underlying the antagonisms of men to men is the question of economics —"the science of ... living well for the state, the family, and the individual," as the Standard Dictionary defines it. While the question of how he shall sustain his mere physical existence—obtain the food, clothes, and shelter so essential to his maintenance—occupies all a man's thought and energy, he does not readily turn toward the consideration of his deeper life. He feels that every man is his enemy, ready and willing to take from him, either by superior sharpness, fraud, or force the opportunity of supplying his needs.

So long as conditions lead anyone to adopt this attitude towards his fellows, he is not apt to give much time or thought to discovering his proper relations toward them. Forces stronger than any number of individuals, acting separately, may drive men into combinations— such as labor organizations among the masses, or large corporations among the privileged classes—until we find a sort of spurious co-operation taking the place of individual effort.

But this co-operation is based upon the necessity of combining to oppose and crush, not upon the desire to avoid friction and bring about harmonious relations between men. Wherever either labor or capital organizes to protect itself from the oppression of the other and to dictate terms to it, that other in its turn organizes to protect itself and to crush the opposing power. Neither party to the struggle sees its dependence upon the other. Capital forgets that labor called it into existence, that without labor there had been no capital, and that should labor cease capital would soon disappear. Labor does not see that capital is its own product, drawn from the land and used to enable men to produce more wealth. And neither sees that the object of producing wealth is not wealth for its own sake, but that man may, through its use, develop himself to an ever higher state.

It is scarcely possible that men should see this under present economic conditions; how, then, can it be possible for men to understand their relations to one another or the advantages of harmony?

And, if economic conditions destroy man's relations to man, how much more completely do they destroy man's relation to the higher life, to Nature or God? Even in his bitterest struggles with his fellows, man recognizes that he and those who oppose him are alike victims of circumstances and must fight. The resentment which he feels is less toward individuals than to the circumstances which make them antagonists when they should be coworkers, and he does not see that the circumstances are of man's own creating.

So long as he regards these conditions as natural, ordained by some power outside himself, he cannot be expected to feel drawn towards closer relations with that power. While he has to watch his chance in the battle of life, he can hardly see that to get in harmony with the laws of the Universe, to recognize his oneness with all life, is to leave struggle and unrest behind. If life is nothing but struggle, he wonders how any attitude can destroy or obviate struggling.

Viewed from his standpoint, he is right. If, as man progresses, the desire to live well strengthens and deepens, and if this desire can be gratified only by waging relentless war against men and conditions, then no study of the relations of man to man or of man to life can lead to anything but greater cunning and more destructive methods of opposition. As the individual finds no way to fulfill his desires without fighting his neighbor, so the nation learns of no way to advance except through crushing other nations. There can rarely be true internal peace for the individual and no true rest and healthy growth for the nation while unjust economic conditions are maintained.

Wherever an individual feels the pressure of economic conditions too keenly he loses what little poise he may have had. He becomes restless and sleepless and the whole tone of his mind and body is lowered. Where the distress from such pressure becomes general, there the nation loses tone; quarrels are readily picked with other nations, and war is resorted to as a means of reducing population and of destroying all forms of wealth, so that a new demand may be created and the economic pressure for a time be lessened. These conditions recur again and again at longer or shorter intervals, and always the same futile means of meeting them is adopted. Man so little understands life that he has not learned that harmony with the laws of the Universe underlies his economic relations as well as his physical relations. If he knew this, he would know that the distress and dissatisfaction common to all nations could come only from the violation of natural laws, and he would begin to search out those laws. Men for a long time held false ideas of the laws of the solar system, and exhausted ingenious devices and systems to explain its phenomena. Then they began to discover underlying laws which explain phenomena more satisfactorily: some of those laws were found, and our knowledge of the solar system to-day is based upon these sure fundamentals.

It is as possible to make sure of the laws governing our economic conditions as of those that govern the solar system. They must lie at the root of all things economic and must explain all phenomena that any condition of society, whether the most primitive or the most complex, can produce. Until these laws are discovered and applied the earth will "turn, troubled in sleep," and men may not know peace.

CHAPTER LII
ECONOMIC REST

Winding up days with toil and nights with sleep.
Shakespeare.

THERE are deep-lying causes of anxiety, unrest, and sleeplessness that more or less affect us all: yet, eighteen hundred years ago, One cried, "The Kingdom of God is at hand." Not, to come eventually, or to future peoples, but "the Kingdom is at hand." We have looked over a world filled with injustice, for the coming of the kingdom—but we have not seen it. What is it that hides "the Kingdom at hand" from our eyes? Is it not iniquity? What kind of iniquity? We once had chattel slavery, which was denounced as "the sum of all villainies." We still have monopoly of the gift of God, which is the fundamental iniquity. For every one of his children a loving father made ample provision in the earth, but we have allowed a few to monopolize it all; some nine out of every hundred own our earth, and we find that, under such circumstances, the laws of God are impracticable; therefore, we say "the Kingdom is not a real Kingdom—it is only in men's minds, only in some far-off imaginable day it may be in their hearts."

The kingdom of God is in our hearts, and, if to-day we will but allow all our fellows to share in the bounty of Nature, the kingdom will be around us also, here and now.

For there is a divine order, a natural law, obedience to which brings its own immediate rewards; disobedience to which involves its own punishment. The first order of Nature is that men should derive their subsistence from the land and the products of land, provided by an all-wise Creator. From what else can we derive it? Does not everything we need, from the wheat to the wheel of the watch, come from the earth? By many hands, by many processes, through many stages, all forms of wealth are obtained by labor from the land. Food, clothing, fuel, machinery, buildings, capital are all results of men working on the materials of the earth. So it is clear why, when we have allowed men to be shut out from that earth, we find ourselves surrounded by poverty and misery.

Like all fundamental laws, the law of our economic relations is simple and easily understood, even by children. It may be stated thus: food, clothes, and shelter, being essential to the maintenance of human life, all human creatures have equal need of and, therefore, equal right to access to the source of food, clothes, and shelter. This source is the earth, and the only method known whereby the earth may be made to yield food, clothes, and shelter is by the application of labor to land. For, no matter what picture we conjure up, whether it be of the farmer tilling the soil, the carpenter building a house, the factory operative weaving cloth, the engineer driving the locomotive that draws the produce to markets—there we find labor. And, if we try to imagine any of these forms of labor as cut off from land, we shall find our very concept of labor and of life wiped out.

Everything necessary to life, whether it be the life of the individual, the nation, or of the whole race, can be produced by the combination of land and labor. Anything that restricts or hampers the application of labor to land leads to suffering on the part of those deprived of this access. When the government of a new country wants to increase population, it offers free land to settlers. It does not say, "If you will come to this country, the government will build mills, factories, stores, offices, banks, and churches for you"; it says rather, "Here is land, come and use it; build for yourselves out of its materials." All other forms of prosperity flow from the application of labor to land, and, therefore, it is sufficient to give to men free access to natural opportunities. If the government of a country owned all the land of that country, it could increase, restrict, or otherwise regulate population, and better or worsen the condition of that population by the way in which it granted or withheld the land under its control.

This is in effect what government has done. It first bettered conditions by allowing free access to land, and then worsened them by allowing a few to make the land their private property; this appropriation of the land carries with it the power to hold it out of use, thus depriving all men of their equal right to the use of the earth, the source of supply for all men's wants. Instead of these favored few being made to pay those deprived of the land an equivalent for the privilege enjoyed, the disinherited many are compelled to pay a premium to the landholder for the opportunity to labor.

When there is a lockout, is it not the pressure of want that brings the men back, hat in hand, to the factory door? If one could go to the outskirts of this town to cultivate a bit of the unused land, could he not hold out till he got all that his labor was worth? And, when he and his fellows are offered less, if they could but get at the unused mines and quarries and coalfields and factory sites, and vacant lots, they would not need to seek an employer at all —they could get credit, if needed, and produce for themselves the capital which they now produce for others and employ themselves in doing it.

So many evils flow from the fundamental wrong of shutting up the earth, that rest, the peace of mind and body that makes for refreshing sleep, is to many impossible.

And who that understands would wish it otherwise? Were the power of rest and peace universal now, it would be a denial of the very cause of rest, —the proper understanding of man's relations to humanity and to life. Until man has adjusted his economic contrivances to the underlying laws of a true Social Science, he cannot have national or racial rest. The material science, biology, is proving this ethical truth. Recently Dr. Woods Hutchinson has shown that it does not take even three generations to make a high-class man a "thoroughbred," as he terms it. If good food, light, air, proper clothing, and wholesome recreation were extended to the masses, each generation would produce its own "thoroughbreds" from the "common people." He says: "Men not only can but do get to be as able, as useful, and as desirable citizens for the community, in every possible regard, in one generation as they will ever get or are capable of becoming. Give the unspoiled, warm-hearted mass of humanity a fair living chance—good food, fresh air, sunshine, decent homes, no overwork, plenty of healthful amusements— and you will reap a far larger crop not merely of happiness, of justice, and of well-being, but also of geniuses, of great men and of all leaders and illuminators than any nation can possibly utilize."

Until the privilege-created aristocracy of other countries and plutocracy of this country get off the backs of the people and cease to exploit them by monopolies, there can be no complete and permanent rest, for the "mania for owning things" possesses the rich, and the fear of want makes restlessness for the poor. The burden-bearing masses have not yet seen the cause of their burden, even though they feel its intolerable weight at times and make efforts to throw it off. All this deepens their unrest.

The very oneness of all life will put sound sleep and true rest ever beyond the general reach until all are given equal opportunity in Nature's great gift to man, the Earth.

Then the worker, free of the taxes of rent and monopoly, free of cut-throat competition forced by monopoly, would have some leisure in which to use his brains and cultivate his affections; and liberty—moral, intellectual, and economic—would be here.

Was it not something like this which Jesus had in mind when he said "the Kingdom of God is at hand"? Did not he say that obedience to the laws of the Universe would bring their own immediate and immense reward? The kingdom and the peace of God is within our reach, did we but realize it.

CHAPTER LIII
"IF HE SLEEP, HE SHALL DO WELL"

Oh! thou best comforter of that sad heart
　　Whom Fortune's spite assails; come, gentle sleep,
The weary mourner soothe.
MRS. TIGHE.

WE believe in a ruling Principle of Order in the Universe, in accordance with which everything lives and moves—planets, plants, and man.

We call this "God," "the Spirit," the "Nature of Things," or by some other name, but we find that, in crystal, vegetable, or animal, it always works: and we see that it tends forever toward a more harmonious arrangement and better relations of the whole system.

There are seeming lapses, where we cannot yet see, in this instance or in that, how it will work out; but in the arrangement of the stars, the growth of knowledge through experience, and in the history of man, we see in the broad view that it does so work out well. Probably Mary, certainly the disciples, thought at the time that the death of Jesus was a horrible mistake and misfortune. Now we see that it was "needful that this one man should die for all the people" and that to him, even then, it was no misfortune. The sacrifice of one for many is a great principle of life. The development of the earth from chaos to fruitfulness, the development of man from brutality to the rule of mind, the development of ourselves from single selfishness to the wider love, shows that there is a beneficent Force and that "all things work together for good." If each of us considers himself alone, as having separate interests, this truth will be obscured; but when we recognize that each of us is a part of the whole, as the tongue is a part of the body, we see that no part can be favored without injuring the entire system.

If we unduly gratify the taste, the tongue is the very first to show that the stomach is "out of order," and this disharmony is felt in the whole body.

Sometimes we have done wrong, or have seen others do wrong apparently with profit; but the wider view will always show that the way of the transgressor is as hard as his heart, that the wicked man is in truth the fool. We know that any attempt that man makes to disturb the right order for the sake of any separate interest must react upon himself, destroying his own happiness as well as the happiness of those about him.

Similarly we see that the prophet, the cultivator, the inventor, the martyr, the benevolent man, each doing what he is inspired to do, is working just as much for all mankind as for himself, that he cannot reap the benefit except as others share it. For our good, we are joined together in one connected whole, so that no man liveth, or so much as dieth, to himself.

We see how the Spirit makes "even the wrath of men to praise him" that the tyranny of a king was necessary to drive out colonists to proclaim liberty, and the fierce rivalry of nations in armament is needed to usher in a Court of International Peace. Since that is so, since we know that in great or universal affairs the eternal purposes cannot be interfered with, why should we think that it fails to work in our own little interests?

We see beautiful, symmetrical shells and well-adapted organs in creatures so small that we know of their existence only through high-power microscopes. In them we find the same rule of law, the same adaptation to supreme ends that we find in the measureless suns and in the measureless souls of men.

Accordingly, when what seems evil "happens," as we say, to us, upon what principle can we conclude that this is an exception, that in this case something has occurred that ought not to have occurred? If one thing went wrong in the divine intent, it would show a limit to the rule of Good. We know that there can be no such limit.

It is not fatalism to believe that the same holy order rules over us, for each of us and each of our efforts is a part of the divine plan, and a means of carrying it out. We should strive for those things that seem to us desirable and good; although we may not have success, as we call it, so kind is the constitution of things that the effort to direct things right dulls the pain of finding that the event shapes itself in a way that we do not like.

We are threatened, perhaps, with what seems a horrible disaster: why, the very derivation of the word disaster refers to the influence which the stars are supposed to have upon our destinies. Some power there is that controls those destinies, in spite of our human limitations of time and space. Who would take the job, though he had the power, of controlling even the material world, arranging the growth of plants, the rise and fall of nations, the birth and waning of the stars?

Yet we do wish to assume just such Omnipotence and Omniscience in our personal affairs; to say that this possession must not, shall not slip from me, this one must not die. And, if this that is so dear does go away, then in that one instance, because it concerns us, we refuse to admit that that instance is no exception to the rule of Love, or to recognize the kind watchfulness of Him that, keeping Israel, slumbers not nor sleeps.

And yet the loss hurts, and the fear of it hurts still more, with a pain that seems past endurance—it hurts, and for ages long it has been necessary that we should have just such pain in order that we may make the efforts that contribute our part to the progress of the world.

But some of us do not in our hearts believe in a beneficent Order of the Universe. We think that some persons may seize what they want, regardless of others, and yet no evil come to them. Even if that be so, still it is wise to act so as to gain the most happiness and, therefore, to accommodate ourselves to the Nature of Things.

If we could but leave out the unreasonable self-pity and get into our hearts, as knowledge that is a part of ourselves, this understanding of the goodness and the loving kindness of God, we should be as gods ourselves, seeing the end from the beginning and recognizing that, success or failure, loss or gain, life or death, the times are in his hands, and it is all very good. And our hearts should not be troubled, nor our rest disturbed.

CHAPTER LIV
CONCLUSION

When the shining day doth die,
   Sweet is sleep.

DORA READ GOODALE.

W E have finished our long inquiry, and it has brought us to thoughts and perhaps to conclusions for which we did not look. Such is the leading of the Spirit, into ways that we know not of.

"So read I this—and as I try
   To write it clear again
I find a second finger lie
   Above mine on the pen."

Much of the ground we have merely passed over, it may be hurriedly, but we have seen a promised land of Peace, and, wherever the soles of our feet have trodden, the land shall be given to us and to our children for an inheritance—if we will.

Now, once again, dear reader—dear, for, in striving and in helping each other to get a clear view of these important matters, we become dear to each other—try these things.

If you have read and merely approved or disapproved, you will get little good from the reading. You remember the pathetically comic story of the little boy who was asked if his father was a Christian:

"Yes," he said, "pa is a Christian; but he does not work much at it." That man might more hopefully have been an infidel. You must put all that you can accept into practice if it is to be of any use.

We have found that what we call body and mind and soul are so closely bound together that no one of them can be well or ill independently of the others. We divide them in our thought and speech; but we cannot find any line of separation. Every state joins on to the next one: mineral and vegetable and animal are composed of the same elements which pass from one state to another. The silex and the lime are taken up to make the wheat hard, we eat wheat and these elements pass into our bones, and, when our bodies return to Mother Earth, the rootlets take them up again to run the round once more.

So the body and mind and soul are all one Life. There are no divisions in Nature. The form differs, but the essence is uniform. We classify for the sake of convenience and of clear statement. As Sir Oliver Lodge says, in "The Survival of Man"—"Boundaries and classifications must be recognized as human artifices, but for practical purposes distinctions are necessary"; but the philosopher never loses sight of the fundamental fact that each animal, flying-fish and whale, seal and polar bear, bat and bird, can be classified only by seizing on some acquired characteristic, such as the temperature of the blood, the method of birth, or the structure of the bones. These mark the animal as belonging to an order.

We see, then, that all are One, different manifestations of the Universal Life, which must be understood and treated as a whole to see and avail ourselves of the Universal Harmony. Accordingly we find that we must work with Nature if she is to bring forth abundantly, of bodily or of spiritual things, to satisfy our desires. Only in the sweat of our faces do we absorb the full comfort and strength of the bread of life.

Whatever you have willingly received, willingly give to others. Only when you cast the seed, this your mental bread, upon the fertilizing waters, shall it return to you in the harvest after many days.

What I have written, I have written as much for myself as for you: if it were not so, it would be useless both to you and to me. We must go up each for himself and take the strongholds of our own Ignorance and Distrust and Fear. Let no one think that he can get life by merely reading these words of life.

Try these things for yourself—teach these things to your other selves; breathe them in and live them out. Open your mind and enlarge your heart so that the Spirit may be able to bless you and keep you with him, and to be kind to you, and to lift up the Light of his countenance upon you and give you

PEACE.

9 781835 915226